Morrow

# ALIENS IN THE SKIES

# ALIENS IN

## *The Scientific Rebuttal to the*

TESTIMONY BY SIX LEADING SCIENTISTS
ON SCIENCE AND ASTRONAUTICS

EDITED AND WITH AN
INTRODUCTION AND COMMENTARY BY

# THE SKIES

*Condon Committee Report*

BEFORE THE HOUSE COMMITTEE
July 29, 1968

John G. Fuller

*G. P. Putnam's Sons   New York*

# ALIENS IN THE SKIES

# Introduction

THREE UFO sightings by United States astronauts Borman and McDivitt are now officially admitted as unexplained by the Condon-University of Colorado Report.

Dozens of other cases in the same report, including those with radar and visual confirmation by experts, are described with such phrases as: "mechanical devices of unknown origin" or "without plausible explanation."

Yet the public has been led to believe by the publication of the Condon Report that the UFO problem has been solved forever.

What the public is barely aware of is that two major scientific schools on the subject of UFOs—flying saucers, if you will—collided within a few months of each other during 1968.

The conclusion reached by Dr. Condon was negative.

The consensus of prominent scientists testifying before the House Committee on Science and Astronautics held that UFOs were unexplained and needed urgent further study.

Far from being closed, the subject is still wide open and completely unresolved.

The occasion of the Congressional UFO hearing had nothing directly to do with the widely proclaimed Colorado UFO study, which was at that time in the process of bungling its way toward the completion of its report for the National Academy of Sciences and the Air Force. As the draft reached its final stages, three key members of Condon's

staff were conspicuously among the missing. Project director
Edward U. Condon, an otherwise brilliant physicist, was
trying to mend fences damaged by a devastatingly reveal-
ing memo written by his managing coordinator, Robert
Low. In the memo outlining the suggested approach to the
Condon-Colorado study, Low had written:

> The trick would be, I think, to describe the project so that, to
> the public, it would appear to be a totally objective study but,
> to the scientific community, would present the image of a group
> of non-believers trying their best to be objective but having an
> almost zero expectation of finding a saucer. . . . I'm inclined to
> feel at this early stage that, if we set up the thing right and take
> pains to get the proper people involved and have success in
> presenting the image we want to present to the scientific com-
> munity, we could carry off the job to our benefit.

The implication was obvious: The Colorado study, judging by the words of one of the men who actively directed it,
seemed to be designed to wink at the whole business of
UFOs, even though the taxpayers were shelling up half a
million dollars for the "trick" of making it "appear" to be a
valid scientific exploration.

When this memo from the open files of the Colorado
study leaked out, Condon responded by firing two of his
best-qualified Ph.D.s and a competent administrative assistant. He made no public statement about his feelings
toward Mr. Low, who had written the rather amazing
memo and who remained on the staff. The blatantly unscientific and biased attitude expressed by this key memo
seemed to make no impression on Dr. Condon, nor did the
word "trick" seem to bother him. He seemed to be disturbed
only by the fact that the memo was made public.

In a veiled reaction to the Condon-Colorado study, however, distinguished men did begin to speak out. They went

on public record during the July 29, 1968 Congressional hearings before the House Committee on Science and Astronautics. Contrary to the attitude of the Air Force-financed-and-sponsored Colorado study, the testimony at the hearings revealed very serious concern about the subject of UFOs from scientists whose background and stature equaled or exceeded that of the Condon group. The House hearing testimony came from a substantial handful of respected scientists who had given considered and open-minded attention to the subject for up to twenty years, in contrast to the Colorado staff, which had plunged into roughly a two-year study with little or no familiarity with the UFO evidence.

Among those testifying before the House committee on that July day were the head of the Department of Astronomy of Northwestern University, a senior scientist of the Institute of Atmospheric Physics of the University of Arizona, an associate professor of astronomy for the Center for Radiophysics and Space Research of Cornell University, the head of the Department of Sociology of the University of Illinois, an associate professor of engineering of the University of California, and a senior scientist for the Computer Sciences Corporation, who was also editor of the *Journal of Astronautical Sciences*. Represented at the hearings by prepared papers were an astronomer from Harvard, a psychologist from the University of Wyoming, a senior research scientist from General Dynamics, a Fellow Scientist of the Westinghouse Astronuclear Laboratory, a psychologist from Stanford University, and the head of the Plant Science Department of Utah State University.

It was an impressive panel, whose studies of an experience with the extensive UFO evidence had led them to speak out frankly on the serious aspects of the subject in the face of widespread scientific prejudice, graphically symbolized by the attitude of the Colorado study.

The consensus of this distinguished panel was that UFOs merited far more attention than that demonstrated by the Air Force-sponsored Colorado study, although the latter was never brought directly into the discussions. Most of the scientists leaned toward the opinion that the extraterrestrial hypothesis could certainly not be ignored, and some openly declared it the most likely hypothesis. Only one member of the group attempted to explain away UFOs as misinterpretations of natural phenomena.

The Congressional hearings of July 29 were significant because up to this point in history any other concentrated attention to the UFO subject in Congress, among officialdom, or in scientific circles, had been brushed off summarily.

The exact reason for this sort of brush-off has never been adequately explained. As a result of it, however, the more intelligent layman and the uninformed scientist have tended to go along with the idea that there must be no real or serious evidence concerning UFOs and that the subject is not worthy of attention.

The prime reason for this lack of concern has been singled out by Dr. James E. McDonald, the physicist from the University of Arizona, as being the impression disseminated by the Air Force—and now the Condon Committee—that the Air Force has applied genuine expertise in examining the UFO evidence and has found nothing to it that would constitute a threat to national security. It is true that there has been no real evidence of any such threat, but the impression that accurate, thorough, and unbiased expertise has been applied to UFOs could not be further from the truth. During the twenty years prior to the Colorado study, an occasional pseudoscientific major or desk sergeant in Dayton, Ohio, would produce "authoritative" statements about sightings from rational and competent witnesses, with only the most cursory examination of the actual facts. But because the Dayton staff allegedly spoke officially for the Air Force, the bulk of the scientific fraternity accepted its word as gospel, and the subject continued to be brushed under the rug for over two decades.

As a result, scientists in this country and all over the world have been not only uninformed but misinformed about a damnably puzzling phenomenon that, whether it turns out to be an extraterrestrial visitation or not, is certainly one of the most important of the century. For if UFOs are a result of mistaken identity, as some who have not thoroughly studied the evidence claim, then the phenomenon demands the most urgent attention of all. It would mean that literally hundreds of pilots, radar technicians, engineers, scientists, and intelligent laymen have been duped by their own senses to such a degree that it is a sheer wonder any sanity at all is left in the world.

This is especially true in regard to the documented sightings by military and commercial pilots and radar men, who depend on accurate observation for their living and for the safety of millions of people. If the cursory explanations forwarded by the Air Force and the Condon Committee are true, then it is a wonder that any plane arrives safely at any airport.

In his introduction to the final report of the Condon Committee, Dr. Condon talks about the UFO Congressional hearing at some length:

Several of the contributors to that symposium have become trenchant advocates in the past several years of a continuing major government investment in a UFO program. Several have long urged a greater degree of congressional interest in this subject. The symposium of 29 July afforded them an occasion on which, with the utmost seriousness, they could put before Congress and the public the best possible data and the most favorable arguments for larger government activity in this field. Hence it is fair to assume that the statements in that symposium represent the maximum case that this group feels could be made. We welcome the fact that this symposium is available to the public and expect that its data and arguments will be compared with those in this report of this study by those whose duty it is to make responsible decisions in this area.

The UFO controversy is now crystallized by the publication of the Congressional Hearings and the Condon Committee Report within a few months of each other. The two camps are sharply opposed, but are certainly of equal scientific rank and stature. The Congressional report clearly states that UFOs are a major concern of science and need immediate serious attention far beyond the limitations of the Colorado study. The Condon Committee seems to reach an entirely different conclusion—but it will be demonstrated here that this negative conclusion lies more in the eyes of the project director, Dr. Condon, than it does in the material actually buried within his report. Shortly after Bantam Books published the Condon Committee Report under the title *Scientific Study of Unidentified Flying Objects*, Dr. J. Allen Hynek, head of the Department of Astronomy of Northwestern University and scientific consultant to the Air Force on the subject of UFOs for over twenty years, wrote me the following:

I just got my copy of the Condon Report and find that in between the lines it is not anywhere as bad as the blatant newspaper accounts had led me to believe. There are a number of cases which even the Condon Committee calls unidentified and they admit that the astronauts on three occasions saw objects they definitely couldn't explain. These points were not brought out in the newspapers.

William James, one of the foremost scientists in American history, once said that in scientifically examining unusual phenomena, all that was necessary was to find "one white

crow" to prove that not all crows were black. In the data unearthed by the Condon Committee, as you will later see,
there are many white crows. All of them, for some strange
reason, seem to escape the attention of Dr. Condon as significant.

In the first page of his report, Dr. Condon states bluntly:

Our general conclusion is that nothing has come from the study
of UFOs in the past 20 years that has added to scientific knowledge. Careful consideration of the record as it is available to us
leads us to conclude that further extensive study of UFOs probably cannot be justified in the expectation that science will be
advanced thereby.

Yet he concedes that his conclusion is controversial, that
three astronaut sightings especially "remain quite unidentified" and are a "challenge to the analyst," and that if UFOs
were discovered to be extraterrestrial, it would be "the
greatest single scientific discovery in the history of man-
kind."

The strange thing is that Dr. Condon had paraphrased a
clearly negative conclusion some two years earlier, just as
the project was getting under way and practically no research had been completed. "It is my inclination right now,"
he is quoted by a reporter for the Elmira, New York, *Star
Gazette* as saying, "to recommend that the government get
out of this business. My attitude right now is that there is
nothing to it . . . but I'm not supposed to reach a conclusion
for another year." Dr. Condon has never denied that statement, although he did, rather lamely, claim that it was taken
out of context.

Both the articulate public and the average scientist have
been victims of many misconceptions about UFOs. Many
of these are covered in detail in the testimony from the new
Congressional hearings that follows. These misconceptions

not only are prevalent but have been responsible for delaying intensive and objective examination of the UFO subject. The Condon Committee report serves only to increase them; while the Congressional hearing testimony helps to clarify them.

As a journalist I have encountered these same misunderstandings on the part of both scientists and laymen. It would seem that if they could be cleared up through logical documentation, the importance of genuine scientific attention to the subject of UFOs would be clear and unassailable. But again, the Air Force and Condon Committee claim that they have employed real scientific objectivity tends to discourage further scientific interest.

For instance, people continually seem to feel that pilots do not report UFOs, when in reality they are constantly reporting them, if not to the public or press, to their commanding officers or to commercial airline executives. It is true that the airlines like to keep the reports out of the papers, because the objects seem to create something of a shock impact to the passengers. It is also true that military pilots and other members of the Air Force are forbidden to discuss their sightings on the threat of both imprisonment and heavy fines. But the documentation is available to anyone who wants to do some digging, and the reports are vivid with articulate detail in literally hundreds of cases, all acknowledged by the Colorado study. Another factor holding back reports from skilled observers is the fear of ridicule. I have talked off the record to both military and commercial pilots who have spoken at length about their sightings, but only on the promise of total anonymity. Case on case of this sort is revealed in the testimony from the hearings on the following pages. To ignore this detailed mass of information would be to indicate a completely closed mind.

Another misconception is the opinion that UFOs are never tracked on radar. They are not only tracked consistently on radar, again as the Colorado-Condon study admits, but often with combined radar and visual sightings by highly-qualified technical personnel. Superficial attempts to explain the radar sightings away as blips or anomalies simply do not match the documentation of the cases where the duration of the sighting is long enough and visual observation is close enough to rule out anything but the structured craft that the better sightings indicate.

Reliable UFO reports over large cities and towns are constant also, yet many people have been led to believe that they are never observed over New York, Chicago, Los Angeles, or equally large centers. I know of one instance where at least four members of the *New Yorker* magazine staff simultaneously observed a UFO at the moment of the famous Northeast blackout. The case was never publicly noted. At almost the same moment, Arthur Rickerby, a *Time-Life* photographer, took a series of color photographs of the New York City skyline, with several of the negatives showing a brilliant unidentified object in the sky that has never been explained. Also at the same moment over New York City, two women in widely separated apartments, unknown to each other, described a strange craft that bore no resemblance whatever to a plane, blimp, helicopter, or balloon. A group of newspaper editors observed an object over the East River near the United Nations, while literally hundreds of people, as you will read later on, have seen low hovering objects over Los Angeles. Reports of this sort are legion, many of them thoroughly documented, yet the misconception continues that UFOs are seen only in isolated areas.

Some otherwise well-informed people think that there are no well-documented photographs of the objects. There are—although a photograph is only as good as the investigation of the photographer, the circumstances, and the negative. There are several that stand up well under the most careful scrutiny, yet the misconception that there are no photographs lingers on. The same ignorance on the part of the public about electromagnetic effects on cars and the strong impact of UFOs on dogs and other animals continues, although most thorough documentation exists.

Marks in the earth, burned areas, or other imprints are often well established by technical personnel in relation to low-altitude UFO sightings, but again many believe that no evidence exists. Care has to be taken that such evidence is not faked, but some cases of this sort have stood up well under the most careful probing, in the face of the wide-spread public disbelief.

One of the most damaging misconceptions was perpetrated when a CBS-TV documentary narrated by Walter Cronkite led an audience of millions to believe that the radar defense network and the satellite tracking system would be sure to pick up UFOs in any portion of the sky. A later denial that such a foolproof system existed did nothing to remove this false belief from the public's mind. Neither telescopes nor radar nor tracking systems are geared to pick up all aerial phenomena; and furthermore, there are many such phenomena that are observed briefly but are unable to be analyzed because the prime work of the instruments is directed toward other interests. A gross misrepresentation such as this, stated with pompous but misled authority on a network documentary, can severely hinder intelligent interest in and scientific investigation of the subject.

Another severely damaging misconception is that created by the later-discounted theory of "marsh gas" as an explanation for the famous Michigan sighting in 1966. This was admitted to be a weak conjecture by the scientist who advanced the theory.

All these misconceptions, plus several others examined at length in the testimony at the Congressional hearings, stem from the pretensions of the Air Force in its claim that it has brought intelligent, unbiased study to bear on UFOs. It can categorically be shown that it has not. Off-the-record remarks to me by reasonably high-ranking officers have indicated that opinion within the Air Force is split—if anything, leaning toward sharp disagreement with the official position, especially among pilots. But the Air Force is joined by two other elements that have been persuasive enough to influence a great many people to believe that UFOs can be easily explained away.

One element is, of course, the Colorado study under Dr. Condon. In addition to the project coordinator's memo, which clearly presented unmistakable signs of prejudice against the subject, Dr. Condon himself repeatedly made public statements that indicated an unusually cavalier attitude. His remarks to the reporter at Elmira, New York, were typical.

He also showed a very strange and intense interest in the marginal and weird reports represented by the lunatic fringe who extol UFOs without taking the trouble to document the sightings they cling to as gospel. Anyone can make a study of this fringe group and come up with a most convincing argument that all UFO observers are emotionally and mentally irresponsible. Yet this group represents only a small fraction of UFO reports, as Dr. Condon admits in his report. Most observers, as he also admits, are sane and responsible, and usually reluctant to make their names public.

It would seem obvious that in the study of UFOs, only those cases reported by competent witnesses should be examined. The reports from the lunatic fringe are obvious and easy to weed out, and the misidentified objects from rational people are usually quickly recognizable as just that. If a scientific marine expedition is out to study the whale, it is useless for it to bring back sharks or mackerel. Yet the preoccupation of the Colorado study with "nut" and

misidentified cases was certainly not much more absurd.
Even though the percentage of "unidentifieds" remains relatively small, there are so many of these that a two-year
study could not possibly cover a thorough investigation of
them. Any time or attention diverted from these hard-core
cases is obviously wasted.

In investigating the Colorado study for an article that was
later to appear in *Look*, I found that many of the staff were
disenchanted and thoroughly disappointed with the cavalier
attitude of both Dr. Condon and project coordinator Low
toward the subject. Admittedly UFOs are extremely difficult
to investigate from a scientific point of view because of the
lack of hardware. But instead of digging in harder, the two
principal men guiding the project often chose to treat the
half-million-dollar probe as a joke and a subject for ridicule.
The fact that the scientists testifying at the recent Congressional hearings do take the subject seriously and are demanding something more durable and broad than the Colorado study is encouraging if their words are not neutralized
by the aura of officialdom that is credited to the final report
of the Condon group. If this happens, still another misconception may be created so that the public will be led
to believe that Condon's conclusions can be taken as gospel.

Another element that has been instrumental in throwing
intelligent people off the course in examining UFOs is represented by the views of Dr. Donald H. Menzel of the Harvard
Observatory. As an astronomer from a leading university,
his words on the subject have been cloaked with the same
aura of authority accorded to the Air Force statements. My
direct contact with Dr. Menzel came during a television
broadcast of a discussion program on NBC-TV that was
ironically titled *Open Mind*. My book *Incident at Exeter*
had just been published, and I was invited to sit with Dr.
Menzel, Dr. J. Allen Hynek of Northwestern, Dr. Leo
Sprinkle of the University of Wyoming, and Dr. Frank Salis-

bury, now of Utah State University. All of these men, incidentally, were represented, either in person or by papers, at the recent Congressional hearings.

The Exeter case had intrigued me as a journalist because it had been an extremely low-altitude sighting, barely higher than a rooftop, of a one-hundred-foot-long object hovering silently over two policemen and a young Navy recruit for a period of at least five minutes, approaching so low that one of the policemen dropped to the ground and pulled his gun. The object was further sighted independently at low altitude by three other persons at other locations, and all observers had been in a temporary state of shock as a result. Further, the case was reported in full on the blotter of the Exeter police station, and two highly regarded officers staked their reputations and jobs on the blotter report.

The television program, moderated by Dr. Eric Goldman of Princeton, at that time academic adviser to President Johnson, centered on the Exeter case because of its unusual character.

I had spent six weeks in the Exeter area, and had not only proved to my satisfaction that the policemen involved were articulate and stable individuals, but uncovered some sixty other sane and sober witnesses who had viewed similar objects at extremely low altitude over a six-week period.

Dr. Menzel began speaking about the case with crisp authority, stating that the policemen were obviously in a hysterical state, that they had obviously been mistaken in their observation, and that the case should be quickly dismissed as not worthy of further attention.

I then began asking Dr. Menzel some questions. How much time had he spent in Exeter investigating the cases? How long had he spent interviewing the officers? Had he visited the site of the incident and asked the men to walk through their experience? Had he examined the police blotter? Had he made random calls around the area to find

other witnesses to the same type of object? And most simple
—what were the officers' names and ages?

As I had suspected, his answers revealed that he had
spent no time whatever in Exeter, had never met the policemen, did not know their names or ages, knew nothing about
their backgrounds or their reputations on the force, and
was reaching all his conclusions on the basis of a stereotyped
Air Force report, which in turn was based on a most superficial inquiry into the case.

When it became obvious that Dr. Menzel was reaching
pseudoscientific conclusions on the basis of entirely superficial knowledge, he responded by shouting loudly over a
nationally syndicated television program; "Will you shut
up!"

From this point on I have been wary of anything that Dr.
Menzel might have to say on the subject, and his telegram
to the House Committee on Science and Astronautics hardly
reduces my credibility gap as far as his views on UFOs are
concerned.

"Received your letter of July," his telegram to the chairman reads, "and will contribute paper* as you suggest. Am
amazed, however, that you could plan so unbalanced a symposium weighted by persons known to favor Government
support of a continuing, expensive, and pointless investigation of UFOs without inviting me, the leading exponent of
opposing views and author of two major books on the
subject."

In the testimony of the hearings, a quotation from a more
open-minded Air Force general is mentioned several times:
"Credible people are seeing incredible things." The attitude
represented by Menzel does nothing to forward intelligent
probing of this tantalizing fact.

A third major force that has discouraged intelligent peo-

* See Appendix I.

ple from pursuing this modern-day mystery is of course the Air Force itself. Several instances of its attitude have already been mentioned. But the most revealing to me was exemplified by my visit to the Pentagon to speak with the colonel in charge of Air Force information on the UFO subject. The occasion also involved the Exeter case.

A portion of my book *Incident at Exeter* was soon to appear in *Look* and later in the *Reader's Digest* under the title "Outer Space Ghost Story." I was extremely anxious to clarify a publicity release sent to the New Hampshire papers by the Pentagon that explained away the Exeter police sighting as "high-flying B-47s or twinkling stars and planets." The effect of this concocted news story was to make the two Exeter officers, one of whom had formerly refueled B-47s from an airborne tanker, appear to be either dismally incompetent observers or out-and-out liars. The police officers had written two letters to the Pentagon protesting this news release, but had received no answer.

The evidence that I had gathered from my six weeks of digging in Exeter was so overwhelming, and indicated that the Air Force's pseudo-explanation was so flimsy, that I wanted to find out if they were honestly misled themselves or whether they were deliberately attempting to discredit the two police officers.

I never did find out completely, but I did discover the basic attitude that has underlain all of the Air Force's statements on the subject. I was ushered to Colonel John F. Spaulding. He greeted me in a large open office where members of the Air Force public relations staff were at work. I pointed out to him that the massive evidence of the Exeter sightings, including his local base commander's report, was strongly at odds with the official Pentagon release on the subject, and that one of the two points of view had to be wrong.

Colonel Spaulding drew himself up to his full height and asked, "Are you calling me a liar?"

The reaction was so totally unexpected that I hastened to explain that all I wanted to do was to justify the discrepancy between two points of view.

He then said, "Sir, you are talking to an officer of the United States Air Force!" Then he turned smartly on his heel and walked off, leaving his staff in dumb amazement.

Several months later, almost the same week the Exeter story appeared in *Look*, the Air Force finally did write the policemen to apologize for its news release which had implied that the men were either incompetents or liars, but I have always wondered about their timing.

The effect that the pompously labeled Air Force statistics have on discouraging proper investigation of UFOs cannot be underestimated. Since 1947, when the more modern UFO sightings began to build up, the Air Force has been issuing statistics of the sightings investigated by it. Over ten thousand reports have accumulated, and the untutored reader is most likely to assume that this is the grand total of all sightings, practically all of which have been explained away as naturally occurring phenomena.

This mass of shaky statistics has again been mistakenly taken for gospel by the bulk of scientists and still continues to shape their attitude toward the subject. Until these statistics are recognized for what they are—unreliable, slipshod, and appallingly incomplete—little progress can be made in persuading scientists as a whole to turn their attention to UFOs.

In the first place, Air Force investigations are as fragmented and incomplete as their statistics, carried out usually by nonscientific personnel in a cursory and desultory manner. I spent some six weeks in Exeter; the Pease Air Force Base in Portsmouth spent not more than two or three hours. In a case near Pittsburgh, a reporter spent over three weeks; the nearby Air Force base made a couple of phone calls. This pattern is constantly being repeated throughout the country.

Beyond this superficial treatment lies the constant proclivity of Air Force investigators to tell even experienced technical observers what they saw, simply on the basis of the observers' own statements. This peculiar trait is most puzzling. One Air Force major told both Ohio and Pennsylvania policemen that they had been chasing Venus, after the officers had made sworn affidavits that they had observed a structured craft at an altitude of not more than a hundred feet over a period of at least an hour. What is strange is how the major could be so definite about an observation that was made when he was sitting in his office at Dayton, especially when the police were joined by other witnesses who independently saw a similar structured object. The same type of maneuvering was attempted by the Air Force in the Exeter case until the *Look* and *Reader's Digest* article appeared.

Even with its effort to explain away the ten thousand sightings in its files, the Air Force reluctantly admits that there are over five hundred cases involving expert observers that it cannot explain. If this were the grand total, the significance would be startling enough. But it is far from the grand total of sightings by highly qualified observers.

Testimony at the Congressional hearings covers the fairly recent Gallup poll concerning the actual number of people who have seen what they believe to be Unidentified Flying Objects. The figure comes close to 5,000,000. This is in rather alarming contrast to the Air Force figure of 10,000. As a matter of fact, the total Air Force figure represents only .002 percent of the total sightings. Applying the Air Force ratio of "unidentified" sightings to total sightings, there would be 250,000 cases that would be impossible to ascribe to natural, easily explained phenomena. Add to this the number of cases kept silent because of embarrassment or the fear of ridicule, and the magnitude of the number of sightings becomes evident. Several times during my investigation in the Exeter area, I had people say to me, "I have never said a word about this to anyone because I don't want people to think I'm a nut."

Most puzzling is the question of why this attitude should prevail in official circles and among many scientists. There are many possible reasons for this, but they are all pure speculation. I am not one who subscribes to a conspiracy theory. It is possible that the Air Force is sensitive about its invulnerability image, is extremely reluctant to admit that it cannot compete with craft that seem to do almost impossible aerial maneuvers. If the Air Force admitted that it could not handle such craft, it would have to admit its own inadequacies, something the military mind is loath to do. The resultant public relations problem, if this is the case, would certainly explain the attempt to downgrade the subject as much as possible.

Scientists are equally loath to try to accept something that can't be put into a test tube or observed on a predictable basis. Further, many scientists do not want to admit the remote possibility that a superior intelligence might exist that would challenge their grasp on the natural world. Others are concerned with the fact that an official announcement indicating the possibility that UFOs are extraterrestrial crafts might cause extensive panic. Those who do feel this way are probably not aware of the extreme curiosity factor, as evidenced by those who encountered low-altitude craft in the Exeter area. Although the first reaction was usually one of shock, this almost immediately wore off and was replaced by curiosity. Nearly everyone who reported a close encounter was out looking again on succeeding nights.

For all practical purposes, only one major scientist has been officially involved with UFOs over the last twenty years, and his position has been lonely, exposed, and vulnerable. Dr. J. Allen Hynek, as the official scientific consultant for the Air Force, has understandably been cautious and conservative in his attitude toward UFOs. But in spite of that, he has been the subject of some criticism from other scientists. His position has been aptly stated in the written statement he submitted to the Congressional hearings:

I cannot dismiss the UFO phenomenon with a shrug. The "hard data" cases contain frequent allusions to recurrent kenmatic, geometric, and luminescent characteristics. I have begun to feel that there is a tendency in 20th century science, to forget that there will be a 21st century science, and indeed, a 30th century science, from which vantage point our knowledge of the universe may appear quite different. We suffer, perhaps, from temporal provincialism, a form of arrogance that has always irritated posterity.

The contrast between this attitude and that expressed by the Condon Committee Report is most vivid.

I went with Dr. Hynek to visit U Thant for a very interesting hour in the Secretary General's office at the UN. The meeting took place shortly after the publication of my story about the Exeter police case in *Look*. The Secretary General was most interested in the reports he had received from countries all over the world about the UFO phenomenon. He questioned Dr. Hynek about the scientific aspects, and me, as a journalist, about the psychological reactions of observers in the Exeter area. One aspect that received considerable attention was how, if indeed UFOs were extraterrestrial spacecraft, they could cover the enormous distance between Alpha Centauri, the nearest star thought to be capable of sustaining a planetary system, and the Earth. This is a factor that many scientists have used to rule out the possibility of such visitations.

A possible answer to this puzzle that came out of the discussion postulated a measurably longer life span on a possible planet in the Alpha Centauri planetary system. If, for instance, a life span could be conceived of as lasting for several hundred or even thousand of our years, the voyage through space at the speed of one of our own spacecraft might not be much more, relatively, than that of Magellan rounding Cape Horn. On earth we have dramatic differences in life span. The fruit fly, or *Drosophila melanogaster*, lives only a few days. The elephant lives over a hundred years. A few hours to an elephant is inconsequential; to a fruit fly it is most of its life. If the same ratio of life span were assumed between inhabitants of an Alpha Centauri planet (elephants), and humans (fruit flies), and if their craft could move at speeds considerably higher than our present craft, it would not be at all illogical to assume that such a journey would be possible.

The meeting with U Thant was most interesting. While the UN has no immediate plans for an international study, the Outer Space Committee of the United Nations would not be averse to such a project if it were forwarded by several scientifically responsible groups in several countries. With the advent of the negative and superficial Condon Report, the chances are diminished that the UN will take action in the near future.

The international character of the UFO phenomenon is one that laymen are often not aware of. Sightings on every continent are manifold and persistent, and just as dramatic and startling as the "hard data" cases of this country.

On a recent trip to France I encountered a case in a village on the Rhone that almost exactly paralleled the Exeter case. On a recent trip I took around the world, including nine countries of Asia, I ran into dozens of reports that were similar to those in this country.

From my own experience in talking to people in many sections of the world, I have found certain questions to be persistent. Foremost among these is: If there are so many UFO reports, how is it that *I* have never seen any?

The answer to this is puzzling, until it is examined logically. There are, for instance, many thousands of UFO sightings a year if the Gallup poll figures are to be believed, several hundred if the Air Force figures are more to your liking. However, there are thirty-five thousand or more fatal automobile accidents a year, and the chances of observing such an incident when it is actually happening are fortunately very small. Or, for instance, there are many reports of sharks being sighted along the coasts every summer. If, however, you were to take a camera and a boat and attempt to photograph a shark's fin in the water, the chances of your encountering one would be slim indeed. So it is with UFOs. Their appearances are unpredictable, and the chances of anyone having a camera with him at the moment of a sighting are relatively slim. In spite of this, there are several photographs that have stood up well under scrutiny and careful investigation, and pictures of this sort taken in different parts of the world have shown remarkable similarities in structure.

As brought out later in this book, the dome-shaped disc is a shape persistently reported, although the varieties of shapes and sizes are many. Very frequently the surface is reported to be metallic, with a hammered-aluminum or pock-marked texture. Lighting patterns seem to change at various speeds and altitudes, but other frequent characteristics noted are pulsating lights around an apparent rim, and brilliantly flashing red and green lights accompanied by nonaerodynamic motion.

Because running lights, strobe lights, and landing lights

on conventional aircraft are often misinterpreted as UFOs, there are certain criteria which can be applied to eliminate honest misinterpretation by intelligent people, and which would reduce the number of cases to those of genuinely puzzling qualities. Naturally, it is important to assume that any sighting is one of a natural phenomenon until every possibility is exhausted.

It is almost safe to assume that any lighting pattern observed moving in a smooth motion across the sky can be eliminated as a UFO, even if the lighting pattern is unusual. In other words, the first law of UFO determination is a law of motion. If the motion is erratic, and the object moves at variable speeds, stops, hovers, makes right-angle turns, ascends or descends like an elevator abruptly without any accompanying sound, the phenomenon is certainly worth checking. Motion of this type eliminates all conventional aircraft except possibly a helicopter, which is easy enough to identify. With motion like this it is also possible to eliminate both weather balloons and those that are frequently used by pranksters.

It is relatively easy for almost anyone to eliminate mistaken identity in regard to flying objects. The large majority of observers are stable, intelligent, and articulate individuals. The ridicule factor has made many of them reluctant to report their sightings officially. The general tendency is to reduce puzzling sightings to natural explanations, but even in spite of that there are many reports which, if the above "law of motion" were applied, would solve the sightings on the spot.

For instance, a friend of mine once called me to report that he had seen a brilliant red object moving across the sky at tremendous speed, leaving a fiery tail behind it. I asked him if the object stopped or hovered, and he replied that it had simply kept moving steadily until it was out of sight. After having conducted so many careful and in-depth interviews for the *Look* story in Exeter, I realized immediately that this could not qualify as a legitimate UFO sighting because of the steady motion. It later turned out to be the famous meteorite that soared over several Eastern states and was viewed by thousands of people. While I did not know about the meteorite at the time, anyone who had taken even a cursory look at the UFO evidence would have immediately eliminated the UFO possibility in this case. Applying the type of investigation that the Condon Committee often conducted, however, much time would have been spent documenting the case, which was essentially worthless as UFO material from the beginning.

Another friend of mine called one night to report that he and his wife had watched a glowing, brilliant orange object moving slowly over his home, an object that suddenly seemed to disappear in a puff of smoke. Again I questioned him about the motion of the object. Did it stop completely and hover? Did it change direction? Did it move up and down or make a sudden turn? When the answers to these questions were negative, it was possible to eliminate the sighting as a UFO worth studying simply on the basis of its smooth motion, and even though it could not be identified immediately as anything logical. Three days later, the local police discovered that some youngsters were sending up surplus weather balloons with lighted candles tied on to the bases. The balloons would move slowly across the sky with the wind, and then ignite and disappear. This is the sort of sighting that no time should be wasted on. Yet the Condon Committee insisted on checking many sightings just as weak as this one when they could have been concentrating on low-altitude cases where the motion and behavior of the object was such that a hoax could immediately be ruled out, and an accurate description of the object could be obtained in detail.

Dr. Condon's preoccupation with the nut and kook cases

was most startling. He sent one member of his staff to cover a man who claimed he was in contact with extraterrestrial intelligence who predicted that a spaceship would land on an exact date and time. Condon personally took a direct interest in several other equally insane cases. Just why he should waste his time on this sort of case when there were hundreds of sightings by pilots, police, and radar men that cried out for investigation has never been explained.

Admittedly the problem with any UFO investigation is that most of it has to rest on testimonial rather than hard-core evidence. This type of anecdotal evidence does not generally make a scientist happy, and Condon was no exception. However, the entire legal system of the country is based on anecdotal testimony, and men have been sent to the electric chair because of it during criminal trials. It is granted that there is good testimony and bad testimony. It is granted that a certain percent of any testimony can be either faulty or false. It is the job of the courts and juries to weed out the good from the bad, to assess the witness at his face value, and to make decisions based on considered judgment.

In assessing UFO reports, judgments such as those utilized by jurists and good journalists must be applied. While naturally hardware is most desirable, the scientist should not wholly disregard testimonial evidence. The field of psychiatry is almost entirely based on this sort of data. What is most needed is the careful scrutiny not only of the testimony, but of the witness himself. When I went to Exeter to research the material for both *Look* and the book *Incident at Exeter*, I was a skeptic about the entire UFO subject. As a journalist, I was determined not to get taken in on any phony story. Consequently, I spent almost as much time checking out the witness himself as I did the details of his reported sighting. There were many questions about each witness that had to be scrutinized. Was the person reasonably stable emotionally? Was he prone to exaggerate or lie? Did he hold a responsible position in the community? Did he have any motive to lie, exaggerate, or create a hoax? How intelligent or articulate was he? Was his observation backed up by other witnesses? How was he regarded by his neighbors, his friends, his family, his minister, if any, or his boss? How intense was his reaction to the sighting? Could he walk through the sighting on location and come up with a reasonably exact and coherent story? Did he avoid eye contact when he answered the questions in the interview? What about his judgment and knowledge regarding aircraft, running lights, air lane patterns in the area? What was his previous interest in the UFO phenomenon? What was the extent of his technical knowledge? How would he answer the same question rephrased later in the interview? Could he be tripped up in the interview? Would he be willing to be interviewed in front of his friends or family? What was his general ability to judge size and distances?

It was of course impossible to get full answers to all these questions for the sixty or more witnesses I interviewed in Exeter. But I could get enough such information to reach a reasonable judgment that the bulk of the people were, on balance, giving straight stories. I was sure before I wrote a line that I was not being taken in as a reporter, and that the material that was unearthed was as valid as it could be under the circumstances. In other words, if this were a criminal case, the evidence assembled could have unquestionably brought in a decision of "guilty" before any judge or jury in the country. The fact that the Air Force was forced to retract its own news release of the Exeter case backed up this assumption.

But in addition to testimonial evidence, there is hard-data evidence accompanying some of the most dramatic and interesting cases and backing up the stories of competent witnesses. Much of this is buried in the Condon Report.

The crux of the problem is to assess through cold logic the total testimony and its accompanying data. Take, for instance, the ten thousand and more reports gathered by the Air Force, forgetting Gallup's figure of five million. Go further and reduce the Air Force figure to the 5 or 6 percent that they acknowledge cannot be explained, the expert technical sightings. Are *all* of five hundred pilots, radar men, police, and other qualified observers at different times and places lying? Are they hallucinating? Are they creating or victims of a hoax? Are they likely to risk their jobs and reputations to insist on swearing that they saw incredible objects? Are they incompetent observers? Are they trying to fool the public?

It is most illogical to assume that they are; in fact, it is downright unscientific to assume this. But in addition, this figure of five hundred is grossly understated. There is evidence that competent and articulate witnesses of closely observed UFOs run into the thousands. If we cannot cautiously accept carefully screened testimonial evidence, we might as well close down all the courts in the country. Even Dr. Condon admits in his report that most UFO witnesses can be accepted as being rational human beings:

In our experience [Dr. Condon writes in the Colorado summary] the persons making reports seem in nearly all cases to be normal, responsible individuals. In most cases, they are quite calm, at least by the time they make a report. They are simply puzzled by what they saw and hope that they can be helped to a better understanding of it. Only a very few are obviously quite emotionally disturbed, their minds being filled with pseudo-scientific, pseudo-religious or other fantasies. Cases of this kind range from slight disturbance to those who are manifestly in need of psychiatric care. The latter form an extremely small minority of all the persons encountered in this study.

The question then emerges, Can five million people or even five hundred experts be *totally* wrong?

With Dr. Condon thus agreeing with the obvious fact that most witnesses are sane and normal, it seems strange that he should ignore such a massive amount of world-wide evidence in reaching his negative conclusion.

A detailed examination of the Condon Report is enough to make anyone stop and ask just how Dr. Condon arrived at this conclusion—and frankly wonder whether he bothered to read the conclusions of his own staff.

Ray Craig, in writing the first chapter on field studies for the Condon Report states: "Some cases involve testimony which, if taken at face value, *describe experiences which can be explained only in terms of the presence of strange vehicles.* . . . These cases are puzzling, and conclusions regarding them depend entirely upon the weight one gives to the personal testimony as presented."[*]

After eliminating many of the cases involving photographs, Colorado staff member William K. Hartmann writes in the Condon Report: "*The residual group of unidentifieds is not inconsistent with the hypothesis that unknown and extraordinary aircraft have penetrated the airspace of the United States,* but none yields sufficient evidence to establish this hypothesis. . . . The present data are compatible with, but do not establish either the hypothesis that (1) the entire UFO phenomenon is a product of misidentification, poor reporting, and fabrication or that (2) a very small part of the UFO phenomenon involves extraordinary events."

In other words, the question is still wide open. This is far from the impression that Dr. Condon's introductory remarks create. And since those remarks are about as far as the bulk of the press needed to go to reach a headline con-

[*] The italics are mine, here and in the following quotations.

clusion, the general public is being left with a misconception that the entire phenomenon is solved.

A section of the Colorado report titled "Indirect Physical Evidence" includes the statement: "Of all physical effects claimed to be due to the presence of UFOs, the alleged malfunction of automobile motors is perhaps the most puzzling. The claim is frequently made, sometimes in reports which are impressive because they involve multiple independent witnesses. Witnesses seem certain that the function of their cars was affected by the unidentified object, which sometimes reportedly was not seen until after the malfunction was noted. *No satisfactory explanation for such effects, if indeed they occurred, is apparent.*"

But the conclusions reached on many of the cases by staff members all through the report are more at odds with Dr. Condon's negative personal opinion than the above, revealing as it is. Of special interest are radar cases, particularly those which are combined with simultaneous visual sightings. Discussing Case #14-N, involving two observations by a Capital Airlines crew of long experience and that of a Northeast Airlines DC-6 crew, Colorado staff member Gordon Thayer writes: "These two similar sightings are very difficult to account for. . . . In summary, *these two cases must be considered unknowns.*"

In Case #1323-B, involving two sergeants of the 753rd Radar Squadron, Thayer concludes: "This case would seem to merit further consideration."

In Case #1206-N, involving a Western Airlines pilot and a GCA radar confirmation of his sighting, Thayer writes: "This case also might merit a more intense investigation."

In Case #5, involving an aircraft sighting confirmed by ground control radar, in which a "radar echo" explanation is first considered, Thayer states: "There are many unexplained aspects to this sighting, however, and a solution such as is given above, although possible, *does not seem highly probable.*"

In Case #1-D, involving the crew of a BOAC Boeing Strato-cruiser, Thayer concludes: "This unusual sighting should therefore be assigned to the category of some almost certainly natural phenomenon, *which is so rare that it apparently has never been reported before or since.*"

In Case #2, involving an RAF pilot sighting, with strong radar confirmation, Thayer concludes: "In summary, this is the most puzzling and unusual case in the radar visual files. *The apparently rational, intelligent behavior of the UFO suggests a mechanical device of unknown origin as the most probable explanation of this sighting.* However, in view of the inevitable fallibility of witnesses, more conventional explanations of this report cannot be entirely ruled out."

In Case #21, involving a Braniff and Continental Airlines plane, combined with radar confirmation, Thayer again invokes an expression of amazement: "This must remain as one of the most puzzling radar cases on record, and *no conclusion is possible at this time.*"

Case #1482-N is most interesting, and perhaps this might be a good place to include some of Thayer's detail. The crew of a Mohawk Airlines DC-3 reported that on June 23, 1955, they were cruising at 3,000 feet at 160 knots when they saw an object about 500 feet above them, moving at "great speed." The body was light gray, almost round, with a center line. Beneath the line, *there were at least four windows,* which emitted bright blue-green lights. They watched it for several miles. The lights "seemed to change color from green to bluish and back again. Just after it went out of sight, *two other commercial airline crews saw the same object.* The Albany control tower reported that it saw the object on Victor 2 airway. *The Boston radar*

*tracked the object on the same airway.* The speed was
computed at 4,500 to 4,800 mph, but no sonic boom was
heard.

Thayer writes in the Colorado findings that this is "a most
intriguing report, *that must certainly be classed as an unknown pending further study, which it certainly deserves.
. . . It does appear that this sighting defies explanation by
conventional means.*" (There is no evidence that Dr. Condon ever ordered further study.)

Summing up the entire section, Thayer states: "There is a
small but *significant* residue of cases from the radar-visual
files . . . *that have no plausible explanation as propagation
phenomena* [false radar images] and/or misinterpreted
man-made objects."

Now if the entire remainder of the Condon Report were
thrown away and these cases alone were considered, it
would seem logically and inescapably impossible to come to
a strong negative conclusion such as Dr. Condon does. How
can anyone—reporter, scientist, pilot, layman—disregard
physical and expert testimonial evidence like this and brush
it into the ash can, as Dr. Condon in essence has done? It
simply does not add up to logic, and especially scientific
logic. These cases and observations are taken from Condon's
own report. Even a cub reporter would not let these drop
without further investigation in full detail.

But this is only the beginning. Available to Dr. Condon
from the research of his own staff, and published in the
Condon Report that he himself has approved, is the following by staff member Franklin E. Roach on the visual
observations *made by several astronauts:*

There are three sightings made by the astronauts
while in orbit which, in the judgment of the writer,
*have not been adequately explained.* These are:

1. Gemini 4, astronaut McDivitt. Observation of a cylindrical object with a protuberance.
2. Gemini 4, astronaut McDivitt. Observation of a moving bright light at a higher level than the Gemini spacecraft.
3. Gemini 7, astronaut Borman saw what he referred to as a "bogey" flying in formation with the spacecraft.

In his evaluation of these sightings by the astronauts, Roach writes in Condon's report:

The training and perspicacity of the astronauts put their reports of sightings in the *highest category of credibility.* They are always meticulous in describing the "facts," avoiding any tendentious interpretations. . . .

*The three unexplained sightings which have been gleaned from a great mass of reports are a challenge to the analyst.* Especially puzzling is the first one on the list, the daytime sighting of an object showing details such as arms (antennas?) protruding from a body having noticeable angular extension. If the NORAD listing of objects near the GT-4 spacecraft is complete as it presumably is, we shall have to find a rational explanation, or alternatively, keep it on our list of unidentifieds.

In the face of this evidence by astronauts—and again forgetting other startling material in the rest of the report—is Dr. Condon's totally negative conclusion justified? Simply on the basis of common sense, few intelligent people would throw this evidence in the wastebasket and forget about it.

Without belaboring the details of some of the other sightings of the Condon Report, which are often perplexing and dramatic, often involve more than one witness, and are often accompanied by radar corroboration, note the conclusions reached on some of these case histories of Condon's own staff:

CASE 2: "In conclusion, although conventional or natural explanation certainly cannot be ruled out, the probability that *at least one genuine UFO was involved appears to be fairly high*."

CASE 6: "*No explanation is attempted to account for the close UFO encounter* reported by three women and a young girl."

CASE 8: "Witness was driving in a rural area in late afternoon, when, he said, a silvery metallic-looking disc with dome, about 30 ft. diameter, descended with wobbling motion into the adjacent valley, hovered just above the ground about 200 feet from the witness, then took off rapidly with a whooshing sound. . . . *The report is unexplained*."

CASE 12: "The case remains *interesting but unexplained*."

CASE 43: "At this point *we leave the original object as unidentified*. . . ."

CASE 46 (*with photographic evidence*): "This is one of the few UFO reports in which all factors investigated, geometric, psychological, and physical appear to be consistent with the assertion that an extaordinary flying object, silvery, metallic, disc-shaped, tens of meters in diameter, and evidently artificial, flew within sight of two witnesses. It cannot be said that the evidence positively rules out a fabrication [of the photograph], although there are some physical factors such as the accuracy of certain photometric measures of the original negative which argue against a fabrication."

CASE 52: "The case must *remain inconclusive*."

CASE 59 (multiple sightings): "Some of the sightings probably were aircraft lights, but generally *no applicable explanation is apparent*."

It would appear, from Dr. Condon's staff's own data above, that the project uncovered not just one white crow, but many.

The fault would thus seem to lie not in the material unearthed and investigated by the Colorado staff—although there is a strong objection to the overlooking of many other baffling cases, while many obviously weak cases were documented in place of them—but the *interpretation* of the results by Dr. Condon.

This is why the hearings before the House Committee on Science and Astronautics, documented in detail on the pages that follow, are so important. The conclusion that further study is urgently needed by the bulk of these opposing scientists is based on scientific qualifications at least equal to, if not stronger than, the Condon study. And there is no question whatever that many of the scientists testifying in the Congressional hearings have invested far more time personally in the field investigations of important UFO cases than Dr. Condon did.

The motive behind Dr. Condon's choosing to brush aside lightly many of the admittedly unidentified cases, many of which were supported by reliable technical data, is hard to discern. It is obvious from the above material that credible people are indeed seeing incredible things.

Two astronauts report three completely unsolved sightings.

A chief staff member writes in the report that those sightings that can't be solved are consistent with the theory that "unknown and extraordinary aircraft have penetrated the airspace of the United States."

Another staff member writes that some of the cases "can be explained only in terms of the presence of strange vehicles."

A key paragraph in the Condon Report states that no

satisfactory explanation exists for the malfunction of automobile motors during certain low-altitude UFO sightings.

At least eight other cases in the Condon Report, some
involving radar confirmation of visual sightings by multiple
commercial or military aircraft, are listed as impossible to
identify.

In line with William James's "one white crow" theory, it
would seem most rational and scientific for the Colorado
study to have dropped all the massive and inconsequential sludge that makes up the bulk of the Condon Report,
and drive hard and exclusively on these cases that are indeed mystifying and incredible. Instead, these cases are
buried so deeply in such a flood of worthless material that
only someone who takes the time to comb the report would
be aware of them.

It is fortunate that the hearings before Congress can, in
part, counteract the obvious bias that Dr. Condon has displayed in his conclusions.

The material in the testimony that follows will help to
answer almost any question that either a skeptic or a believer could ask. At the same time it suggests a conclusion
in direct opposition to that of the Condon Report.

# 1.

THE hearings before the House Committee on Science and Astronautics began with little fanfare at 10:05 A.M. on July 29, 1968, in room 2318 of the Rayburn House Office Building. Congressman J. Edward Roush of Indiana, as acting chairman of the symposium, called the meeting to order.

It had been emphasized at the beginning that the six scientists present were in no way directly disputing the methods employed by the Condon Committee, even though there were a lot of tacit rumblings as the result of the "trick" memo and other evidence that all was not calm on the Colorado campus. On this July day no one yet knew what the conclusions of the Condon Report would be. But the straws in the wind without question pointed toward a whitewash for the ambiguous Air Force position.

Congressman Roush's opening remarks were quiet and restrained, emphasizing that the Committee on Science and Astronautics took no clear stand on the UFO problem and that the committee was there to learn and listen. Representative George P. Miller of California, the overall chairman of the committee, confirmed this viewpoint, and emphatically pointed out that the hearing was in no way to be construed as a criticism of the way the Air Force was handling the UFO problem.

Mr. ROUSH. Today the House Committee on Science and Astronautics conducts a very special session, a symposium on the subject of unidentified flying objects; the name of which is a reminder to us of our ignorance on this subject and a challenge to acquire more knowledge thereof.

We approach the question of unidentified flying objects as purely a scientific problem, one of unanswered questions. Certainly the rigid and exacting discipline of science should be marshaled to explore the nature of phenomena which reliable citizens continue to report.

A significant part of the problem has been that the sightings reported have not been accompanied by so-called hardware or materials that could be investigated and analyzed. So we are left with hypotheses about the nature of UFO's. These hypotheses range from the conclusion that they are purely psychological phenomena, that is, some kind of hallucinatory phenomena; to that of some kind of natural physical phenomena; to that of advanced technological machinery manned by some kind of intelligence, that is, the extraterrestrial hypotheses.

With the range in mind, then, we have invited six outstanding scientists to address us today, men who deal with the physical, the psychological, the sociological, and the technological data relevant to the issues involved. We welcome them and look forward to their remarks. Additionally we have requested several other scientists to make their presentations in the form of papers to be added to these when published by the committee.

We take no stand on these matters. Indeed, we are here today to listen to their assessment of the nature of the problem; to any tentative conclusions or suggestions they might offer, so that our judgments and our actions might be based on reliable and expert information. We are here to listen and to learn.

Events of the last half century certainly verify the American philosopher, John Dewey's conclusion that "Every great advance in science has issued from a new audacity of imagination." With an open and inquiring attitude, then, we now turn to our speakers for the day.

They will include: Dr. J. Allen Hynek, head of the Department of Astronomy, Northwestern University; Dr. James E. McDonald, senior physicist, the Institute of Atmospheric Physics, the University of Arizona; Dr. Carl Sagan, Department of Astronomy and Center for Radiophysics and Space Research, Cornell University; Dr. Robert L. Hall, head of the Department of Sociology, University of Illinois at Chicago; Dr. James A. Harder, associate professor of civil engineering, University of California at Berkeley, and Dr. Robert M. L. Baker, Jr., Computer Sciences Corp. and Department of Engineering, UCLA.

Gentlemen, we welcome your presentations. We ask you to speak first, Dr. Hynek, followed by Dr. McDonald, and then Dr. Sagan. This afternoon Dr. Hall will commence our session, followed by Dr. Harder and then Dr. Baker. The subject matter of the presentations determines the order in which you speak. We hope at the end of the day to allow the six of you to discuss the material presented among yourselves and with the committee in a kind of roundtable discussion.

Mr. Chairman—the chairman of our full committee, Mr. George Miller.

Chairman MILLER. I want to join in welcoming you here. I want to point out that your presence here is not a challenge to the work that is being done by the Air Force, a particular agency that has to deal with this subject.

Unfortunately there are those who are highly critical of the Air Force, saying that the Air Force has not approached this problem properly. I want you to know that we are in no way trying to go into the field that is theirs by law, and thus we are not critical of what the Air Force is doing.

We should look at the problem from every angle, and we are here in that respect. I just want to point out we are not here to criticize the actions of the Air Force.

Thank you.

Mr. ROUSH. I think it is only appropriate that Dr. Hynek be introduced by our colleague, Mr. Rumsfeld.

Mr. Rumsfeld.

Mr. RUMSFELD. Thank you, Mr. Chairman.

It is a pleasure to welcome all the members of this distinguished panel, and particularly to welcome Dr. Allen Hynek, who is a son of Illinois, and presently serves in the Department of Astronomy and Director of the Lindheimer Astronomical Research Center. Dr. Hynek is a member of a number of scientific societies, and has served in the Government service as well as in the academic community. As his Congressman I am delighted he has been invited to appear on this panel, and we certainly look forward to his comments.

Thank you, Mr. Chairman.

Mr. ROUSH. Dr. Hynek, the floor is yours.

Hynek's specialty is astrophysics, and his work in stellar spectroscopy, F-type stars, and satellite tracking is extensive.

As the scientific consultant for the Air Force on the subject of UFOs for some twenty years, he held a unique position. Falling into this sideline job almost by accident, he began to find the sheer weight of accumulated data extremely heavy for one lone scientist to bear. For while a large majority of the cases could easily be explained by natural phenomena, the residue of unexplained cases was most bothersome. Equally distressing was the fact that there was no hardware to crystallize a genuine scientific solution, and at the same time there was no other scientist to share with him the official load of the swarm of Air Force cases.

In the testimony, he tells his own story in revealing terms.

Dr. HYNEK. Thank you.

My name is J. Allen Hynek. I am professor of astronomy at Northwestern University, Evanston, Ill., where I serve as chairman of the department of astronomy and director of the Lindheimer Astronomical Research Center. I have also served for many years, and still do, as scientific consultant to the U.S. Air Force on Unidentified Flying Objects, or UFO's. Today, however, I am speaking as a private citizen and scientist and not as a representative of the Air Force.

We are here today, I gather, to examine whether the UFO phenomenon is worthy of serious scientific attention. I hope my comments may contribute to your understanding of the problem and help lead to its eventual solution.

The UFO problem has been with us now for many years. It would be difficult to find another subject which has claimed as much attention in the world press, in the conversation of people of all walks of life, and which has captured the imagination of so many, over so long a period of time. The word UFO, or flying saucer, can be found in the languages and dictionaries of all civilized peoples, and if one were to collect all the words that have been printed in newspapers, magazines, and books in the past two decades, it would be a staggering assemblage. The bibliography of the subject recently compiled at the Library of Congress is a most impressive document, and illustrates that the UFO became a problem for the librarian even before it did for the scientist.

As we all know, the scientific world is a world of exact calculations, of quantitative data, of controlled laboratory experiments, and of seemingly well-understood laws and principles. The UFO phenomenon does not seem to fit into that world; it seems to flaunt itself before our present-day science.

The subject of UFO's has engendered an inordinate emotional reaction in certain quarters and has far more often called forth heated controversy rather than calm consideration. Most scientists have preferred to remain aloof from the fray entirely, thereby running the risk of "being down on what they were not up on," as the old adage goes.

It is unlikely that I would have become involved in the study of the UFO phenomenon had I not been officially asked to do so. I probably would have—and in fact did for a time—regarded the whole subject as rank nonsense, the product of silly seasons, and a peculiarly American craze that would run its course as all popular crazes do.

I was asked by the Air Force 20 years ago to assist them, as an astronomer, in weeding out those reports arising from misidentification of planets, stars, meteors, and other celestial objects and events. In the course of doing my "homework" I found that some 30 percent of the then current cases very probably had astronomical causes, but my curiosity was aroused by some of the patently nonastronomical reports.

These were ostensibly being explained by the consultant psychologist, but I frequently had the same feeling about the explanations offered for some of these cases that I have had when I have seen a magician saw a woman in half. How he did it was beyond my own field of competence, but I did not question his competence. Yes, I was quite sure that he did not actually saw the woman in half!

My curiosity thus once aroused led me to look into reports other than those of a purely astronomical nature, and in the course of years I have continued to do so. I have pondered over the continuing flow of strange reports from this and a great many other countries, for it is a gross mistake to think that the United States has any exclusive claim to the UFO phenomenon.

Those reports which interested me the most—and still do —were those which, apparently written in all seriousness by articulate individuals, nonetheless seemed so preposterous as to invite derisive dismissal by any scientist casually introduced to the subject. Such baffling reports, however, represent a relatively small subset of reports. I did not— and still do not—concern myself with reports which arise from obvious misidentifications by witnesses who are not aware of the many things in the sky today which have a simple, natural explanation. These have little scientific value, except perhaps to a sociologist or an ophthalmologist; it matters not whether 100 or 100,000 people fail to identify an artificial satellite or a high-altitude balloon.

The UFO reports which in my opinion have potential scientific value are those—and this may serve us as a working definition of UFO's—are those reports of aerial phenomena which continue to defy explanation in conventional scientific terms. Many scientists, not familiar with the really challenging UFO data, will not accept the necessity for a high order of scientific inquiry and effort to establish the validity of the data—and therefore such detailed, conscientious, and systematic inquiry has yet to be undertaken.

We cannot expect the world of science to take seriously the fare offered at airport newsstands and paperback shelves.

I have been asked by some why, as consultant to the Air Force for so many years, I did not alert the scientific world to the possible seriousness of the UFO problem years ago. The answer is simple; a scientist must try to be sure of his facts. He must not cry "wolf" unless he is reasonably sure there is a wolf.

I was painfully aware, and still am, of the amorphous

nature of the UFO data, of the anecdotal nature of UFO reports, of the lack of followup and serious inquiry into reports (which would have required a large scientific staff and adequate funding), of the lack of hardware, of the lack of unimpeachable photographic evidence, and of the almost total lack of quantitative data—of all those things which are part and parcel of the working environment of the scientist.

I was aware that in order to interest scientists, hard-core data were needed, and, while the store of unquestionably puzzling reports from competent witnesses continued to grow the wherewithal to obtain such hard-core data which would, once and for all, clinch the matter, was not forthcoming. Thus my scientific reticence was based on a carefully weighed decision.

In attempting analysis of the UFO problem today, I pay particular attention to reports containing large amounts of information which are made by several witnesses, if possible, who as far as I can ascertain, have unimpeachable reputations and are competent. For example, I might cite a detailed report I received from the associate director of one of the Nation's most important scientific laboratories, and his family.

Reports such as these are obviously in a different category from reports which, say, identify Venus as a hovering spaceship, and thus add to the frustrating confusion.

On the other hand, when one or more obviously reliable persons reports—as has happened many times—that a brightly illuminated object hovered a few hundred feet above their automobile, and that during the incident their car motor stopped, the headlights dimmed or went out, and the radio stopped playing, only to have these functions return to normal after the disappearance of the UFO, it is clearly another matter.

By what right can we summarily ignore their testimony and imply that they are deluded or just plain liars? Would we so treat these same people if they were testifying in court, under oath, on more mundane matters?

Or, if it is reported, as it has been in many instances over the world by reputable and competent persons, that while they were sitting quietly at home they heard the barnyard animals behaving in a greatly disturbed and atypical manner and when, upon investigating, found not only the animals in a state of panic but reported a noiseless—or sometimes humming—brightly illuminated object hovering nearby, beaming a bright red light down onto the surroundings, then clearly we should pay attention. Something very important may be going on.

Now, when in any recognized field of science an outstanding event takes place, or a new phenomenon is discovered, an account of it is quickly presented at a scientific meeting or is published in a respected appropriate journal. But this is certainly not the case with unusual UFO reports made by competent witnesses.

There appears to be a scientific taboo on even the passive tabulation of UFO reports. Clearly no serious work can be undertaken until such taboos are removed. There should be a respectable mechanism for the publication, for instance, of a paper on reported occurrences of electromagnetic phenomena in UFO encounters.

It would be foolhardy to attempt to present such a paper on UFO's to the American Physical Society or to the American Astronomical Society. The paper would be laughed down, if all that could be presented as scientific data were the anecdotal, incomplete, and nonquantitative reports available. Consequently reports of unexplainable UFO cases are likely to be found, if at all, in pulp magazines and paperbacks, of which the sole purpose of many seems to be, apart from making a fast buck for the authors, to titillate the fancy of the credulous.

Indeed, in such newsstand publications three or four UFO

reports are frequently sensationalized on one page with gross disregard for accuracy and documentation; the result is that a scientist—if he reads them at all—is very likely to suffer mental nausea and to relegate the whole subject to the trash heap.

This is the first problem a scientist encounters when he takes a look at the UFO phenomenon. His publicly available source material is almost certain to consist of sensational, undocumented accounts of what may have been an actual event. Such accounts are much akin, perhaps, to the account we might expect from an aborigine encountering a helicopter for the first time, or seeing a total eclipse of the sun. There is nowhere a serious scientist can turn for what he would consider meaningful, hard-core data—as hard core and quantitative as the phenomenon itself permits at present.

Here we come to the crux of the problem of the scientist and the UFO. The ultimate problem is, of course, what are UFO's; but the immediate and crucial problem is, How do we get data for proper scientific study? The problem has been made immensely more difficult by the supposition held by most scientists, on the basis of the poor data available to them, that there couldn't possibly be anything substantial to UFO reports in the first place, and hence that there is no point to wasting time or money investigating.

This strange, but under the circumstances understandable attitude, would be akin to saying, for instance, let us not build observatories and telescopes for the study of the stars because it is obvious that those twinkling points of light up there are just illusions in the upper atmosphere and do not represent physical things.

Fortunately, centuries ago there were a few curious men who did not easily accept the notion that stars were illusory lights on a crystalline celestial sphere and judged that the study of the stars might be worthwhile though, to many, a seemingly impractical and nonsensical venture. The pursuit of that seemingly impractical and possibly unrewarding study of astronomy and related sciences, however, has given us the highly technological world we live in and the high standard of living we enjoy—a standard which would have been totally impossible in a peasant society whose eyes were never turned toward the skies.

Can we afford not to look toward the UFO skies; can we afford to overlook a potential breakthrough of great significance? And even apart from that, the public is growing impatient. The public does not want another 20 years of UFO confusion. They want to know whether there really is something to this whole UFO business—and I can tell you definitely that they are not satisfied with the answers they have been getting. The public in general may be unsophisticated in scientific matters, but they have an uncanny way of distinguishing between an honest scientific approach and the method of ridicule and persiflage.

As scientists, we may honestly wish to see whether there is any scientific paydirt in this international UFO phenomenon. But to discover this paydirt we must devote serious study to UFO's. To make serious study possible, however, requires recruiting competent scientists, engineers, and technical people, as well as psychologists and sociologists.

This in turn requires not only funds but a receptive scientific climate. Many scientists have expressed to me privately their interest in the problem and their desire to actively pursue UFO research as soon as the scientific stigma is removed. But as long as the unverified presumption is strongly entrenched that every UFO has a simple, rational everyday explanation, the required climate for a proper and definitive study will never develop.

I recall an encounter I had sometime ago with the then chief scientist at the Pentagon. He asked me just how much longer we were "going to look at this stuff." I reminded him that we hadn't really looked at it yet—that is, in the sense, say, that the FBI looks at a kidnapping, a bank robbery, or a narcotics ring.

Up to this point I have not discussed another major impediment to the acceptance of the UFO phenomenon as legitimate material for scientific study. I refer to the adoption of the UFO phenomenon by certain segments of the public for their own peculiar uses. From the very start there have been psychically unbalanced individuals and pseudo-religious cultist groups—and they persist in force today—who found in the UFO picture an opportunity to further their own fanciful cosmic and religious beliefs and who find solace and hope in the pious belief that UFO's carry kindly space brothers whose sole aim is a mission of salvation.

Such people "couldn't care less" about documentation, scientific study, and careful critical consideration. The conventions and meetings these people hold, and the literature they purvey, can only be the subject of derisive laughter and, I must stress, it is a most serious mistake for anyone to confuse this unfortunate aspect of the total UFO phenomenon with the articulate reports made by people who are unmistakably serious and make their reports out of a sense of civic duty and an abiding desire to know the cause of their experience.

It may not be amiss here to remark in passing that the "true believers" I have just referred to are rarely the ones who make UFO reports. Their beliefs do not need factual support. The reporters of the truly baffling UFO's, on the other hand, are most frequently disinterested or even skeptical people who are taken by surprise by an experience they cannot understand.

Hopefully the time is not far off when the UFO phenomenon can have an adequate and definitive hearing, and when a scholarly paper on the nature of UFO reports can be presented before scientific bodies without prejudice. Despite the scientific attitude to this subject in the past, I nevertheless decided to present a short paper on UFO's to a scientific body in 1952, following a scientific hunch that in the UFO phenomenon we were dealing with a subject of great possible importance.

In my paper (Journal of the Optical Society of America 43, pp. 311–314, 1963), which I should like to have read into the record, I made reference to the many cases in 1952 and earlier which were nonastronomical in nature and did not seem to have a logical, ready explanation.

In his article Dr. Hynek indicated that it was a "matter of scientific obligation and responsibility" to examine seriously reputable reports from responsible witnesses, in spite of the seemingly fanciful character of the objects. He personally examined several hundred reports that did not have any ready or obvious explanation. He limited these cases to those that have been "observed by two or more people, at least one of whom is practiced in the making of observations of some kind"—such as pilots, control tower operators, weather observers, scientists, and so forth.

He cites one example where several Air Force airmen watched a bright object approach at a very slow speed, halt nearly overhead, then reverse direction with no apparent turn. Three other objects were observed on two other nights over a period of some ten minutes. There were ten airmen involved, including a control tower operator, an aircraft dispatcher, and two pilots from Wright Field. He describes several other multiple-witness cases, several combining visual observation with distinct radar confirmation. One articulate description by an Air Force lieutenant is particularly vivid, involving six metallic discs in strange maneuvers.

Dr. Hynek concludes his article by saying: "I submit that this Air Force lieutenant was not incompetent, but rather that his manner of reporting—as far as it went—was commendable and that his report made in good faith, is therefore entitled to a hearing without prejudice or ridicule, but also, without fanfare, hysteria, and fantastic newspaper publicity."

Dr. Hynek's verbal testimony continues:

Dr. HYNEK. I cautioned against the then prevalent attitude of ridicule, pointing out that the UFO phenomenon, which had generated vast public interest, represented an unparalleled opportunity to demonstrate to the public the operation of the scientific method in attacking a problem, and that "ridicule is not a part of the scientific method and the public should not be taught that it is."

In those years and the following ones I repeatedly asked for the upgrading of the method of reporting UFO's to the Air Force. In 1960, in a hearing before Congressman Smart and his committee I urged "immediate reaction capabilities" in the investigation of UFO reports. The recommendation was applauded but not funded.

As the scientific climate grew more receptive in giving the UFO phenomenon a scientific hearing, I published a letter in "Science" (Oct. 21, 1966), not without difficulty, in which I pointed out the following general misconceptions regarding UFO's.

One great misconception is that only UFO buffs report UFO's; quite the opposite is the case, as is the misconception that the most baffling reports come from unreliable, unstable, and uneducated people. Most reports of this baffling sort which I at least receive in my mail, are remarkably articulate.

Other misconceptions are that UFO's are never reported by scientifically trained people, are never seen at close range, have never been detected on radars, and have never been recorded by scientific cameras.

It is well to remind ourselves at this point of the definition of an UFO: those aerial phenomena reports which continue to defy explanation in conventional scientific terms, even after appropriate study. There is no point to be interested in anything else; lights at night which might be aircraft, balloons, meteors, or satellite re-entries—all these fit more readily into the category of IFO's or identified flying objects.

In other words, only truly unidentified cases should be of interest. The Air Force has its own definition of an unidentified case, and it has many hundreds in its files. The Air Force calls a sighting unidentified when a report apparently contains all pertinent data necessary to suggest a valid hypothesis concerning the cause or explanation of the report but the description of the object or its motion cannot be correlated with any known object or phenomenon.

It is most logical to ask why do not the unidentified in the Air Force files call forth investigative efforts in depth and of wide scope. The answer is compound: the Air Force position is that there is no evidence that UFO's represent a threat to the national security; consequently it follows that it is not their mission to be scientifically curious about the hundreds of unidentified cases in their own files.

It may be that, properly investigated, many of the Air Force unidentifieds would turn out to be IFO's after all, but it is illogical to conclude that this would be true of all unidentified reports. As long as unidentified cases exist, thus bona fide UFO's according to definition, we don't know what they are, and these should represent a remarkable challenge to science and an open invitation to inquiry.

But so powerful and all-encompassing have the misconceptions among scientists been about the nature of UFO information that an amazing lethargy and apathy to investigation has prevailed. This apathy is unbecoming to the ideals of science and undermines public confidence.

Now it is of interest to report that in just the past few years, probably because of the persistent flow of UFO reports from this and many other countries (one could base his whole plea for a major investigative effort solely on the reports of the years 1966 and 1967) there has been a growing but unheralded interest on the part of more and more scientists, engineers, and technicians in doing something positive about the UFO problem. To this growing body of qualified people it seems increasingly preposterous to allow another two decades of confusion to exist.

The feeling is definitely on the increase that we should either fish or cut bait, that we should mobilize in earnest adequate groups of scientists and investigators, properly funded, adopt a "we mean business" attitude, or drop the whole thing. My recommendation is to fish.

As a scientist I can form conclusions from and act upon only reliable scientific data. Such data are extremely scarce in the UFO field for reasons already pointed out: it has never been considered worthwhile to improve the data-gathering process because the whole subject has been pre-judged. Even as a scientist, however, I am permitted a scientific hunch, and that hunch has told me for some time, despite the tremendous muddiness of the scientific waters in this area, the continued reporting from various parts of the world of unidentified flying objects, reports frequently made by people of high repute who would stand nothing whatever to gain from making such reports, that there is scientific paydirt in the UFO phenomenon—possibly extremely valuable paydirt—and that therefore a scientific effort on a much larger scale than any heretofore should be mounted for a frontal attack on this problem.

In saying this I do not feel that I can be labeled a flying saucer "believer"—my swamp gas record in the Michigan UFO melee should suffice to squash any such ideas—but I do feel that even though this may be an area of scientific quicksand, signals continue to point to a mystery that needs to be solved. Can we afford to overlook something that might be of great potential value to the Nation?

I am reminded of the old story of the member of Parliament who visited Faraday's laboratory where he was at work on early experiments on electrical induction. When asked of what possible value all this might have, Faraday replied, "Sir, someday you may be able to tax it."

Apart from such inducements, I have the following recommendations to make: first, that a mechanism be set up whereby the problem posed by the reports from all over the world, but especially by those in the United States, from people of high credibility, can be adequately studied, using all methods available to modern science, and that the investigation be accorded a proper degree of scientific respectability and an absence of ridicule so that proper investigations can be carried out unhampered by matters not worthy of the ideals of scientific endeavor. I might suggest that this could be accomplished by the establishment, by the Congress, of a UFO Scientific Board of Inquiry, properly funded, for the specific purpose of an investigation in depth of the UFO phenomenon.

Secondly, I recommend that the United States seek the cooperation of the United Nations in establishing a means for the impartial and free interchange among nations of information about, and reports of, unidentified flying objects —a sort of international clearinghouse for the exchange of information on this subject. For, since the UFO phenomenon is global, it would be as inefficient to study it without enlisting the aid of other nations as it would be to study world meteorology by using weather reports from one country alone.

Now, it may be well to remind ourselves at this point, that the UFO problem may not lend itself to an immediate solution in our time. The problem may be far more complex than we imagine. Attempts to solve it may be no more productive than attempts to solve the problem of the Aurora Borealis would have been 100 years ago.

The cause of northern lights could not have been determined in the framework of the science of 1868. Scientific knowledge in those days was not sufficient to encompass the phenomenon.

Similarly, our scientific knowledge today may be grossly insufficient to encompass the problem posed by UFO's. A profound scientific obligation exists, nonetheless, to gather the best data possible for scientific posterity.

To summarize: in the course of 20 years of study of UFO reports and of the interviewing of witnesses, I have been led to a conclusion quite different from the one I reached in the very first years of my work. At first I was negatively impressed with the low scientific content of UFO reports, with the lack of quantitative data, with the anecdotal nature of the reports, and especially with the lack of hardware, of unimpeachable photographs, and with the lack of instrumental recordings.

I am still aware of the paucity of truly hard-core data— but then, no effort has really been made to gather it. Nonetheless, the cumulative weight of continued reports from groups of people around the world whose competence and sanity I have no reason to doubt, reports involving close encounters with unexplainable craft, with physical effects on animals, motor vehicles, growing plants, and on the ground, has led me reluctantly to the conclusion that either there is a scientifically valuable subset of reports in the UFO phenomenon or that we have a world society containing people who are articulate, sane, and reputable in all matters save UFO reports.

Either way, I feel that there exists a phenomenon eminently worthy of study. If one asks, for what purpose, I can only answer—how does one ever know where scientific inquiry will lead. If the sole purpose of such a study is to satisfy human curiosity, to probe the unknown, and to provide intellectual adventure, then it is in line with what science has always stood for.

Scientific inquiry has paid off, even though pioneers like Faraday, Curie, Hahn, Pasteur, Goddard, and many others little realized where the paths they blazed would lead. As far as UFO's are concerned, I believe we should investigate them for the simple reason that we want to know what lies behind this utterly baffling phenomenon—or even more simply, we want to find out what it's all about.

Thank you.

Mr. ROUSH. Thank you, Dr. Hynek.

Although we have reserved the latter part of the afternoon for our roundtable discussion, the Chair is well aware the Members of Congress, because of other duties, may not find it possible to be here during that time.

If any of my colleagues do have questions and can keep them brief, which I realize is impossible, I will entertain those questions at this time. But keep in mind that we have two more papers this morning, and three this afternoon.

Mr. HECHLER. Mr. Chairman.

Mr. ROUSH. Mr. Hechler.

Mr. HECHLER. First I would like to commend you, Mr. Roush, for your initiative in setting up this symposium.

I would like to ask you, Dr. Hynek, whether you consider this scientific board of inquiry which you outlined as a sort of a one-shot thing which would make its report, or do you consider this to be a continuing body that could examine, as the Air Force has, reports and analyze them? And with this question, I would like to ask if your assumption is that the Air Force, because of its emphasis on national security, has really not measured up to a thorough scientific analysis of UFO's?

Dr. HYNEK. Well, in answer to the first part of that question, sir, I would say I don't believe in a problem as complex as this the one-shot approach would be sufficient. I think there should be this board of inquiry which should be a continuing board in the same sense that we have, I presume, boards of study for world population problems, of pollution problems, of world health, and so forth.

The letter that came with the invitation to speak here, strongly stated that we would not discuss the Air Force participation in these matters, and I would like to therefore not speak to that point.

Mr. ROUSH. Mr. Rumsfeld.

Mr. RUMSFELD. Because of the fact it does look as though we will have a busy afternoon on the floor, I very likely will not be present for the remainder of the discussion. I would like to express the hope the other members of the panel might at some point comment on the two recommendations that Dr. Hynek has set forth in his paper. Further, I would hope that each member of the panel, during the afternoon session, might address himself to the questions of priorities.

Assuming that there is some agreement with Dr. Hynek's conclusion that this is an area worthy of additional study, then the question for Congress, of course, becomes what is the priority? This is a rather unique situation in that it is a scientific question that has reached the public prior to the time that anything beneficial can even be imagined. In many instances a scientific effort is not widely known to the public until it is successful.

Each of you are experts in one or more disciplines. I am sure there are a number of things on your shopping lists for additional funding. I would be interested to know how this effort that is proposed here might fit into your lists of priorities.

Thank you, Mr. Chairman.

Mr. ROUSH. Thank you, Mr. Rumsfeld.

Mr. Miller.

Chairman MILLER. Doctor, you mentioned a number of things—population studies at least. A great many of these are carried out not by Government directly, but in the National Science Foundation or through the National Academy of Sciences or scientific bodies themselves.

Do you think, I merely offer this as a suggestion, perhaps the scientific community try to encourage NSF or the scientific societies dealing in this field to take the initiative in doing this, rather than to wait for Government to take the initiative?

Dr. HYNEK. I know, of course, most of the bodies you have mentioned are funded by the Government anyway. Most or a great part of our scientific research today has to be so funded. Private sources are certainly not sufficient. And, therefore, I think it is rather academic, really, to worry too much about who does it. It is more a question of who is going to pay for it.

We have a rather interesting situation here, as Congressman Rumsfeld has already pointed out. This is one of those strange situations in which the cart is sort of before the horse. Generally this results in the scientific laboratories and the results of the studies of scientists finally come to the public attention, but here we have the other situation. It is the public pressure, the public wants to know actually, more than the scientists, at the moment. So you are facing public pressures, even, definitely more than scientific pressures at the moment.

Chairman MILLER. Unfortunately in some of our problems, for example the NASA problems, where the public is indifferent, the matter of waste disposal, pollution, health, and these things. They are quite indifferent to them, and it takes a lot of effort to get them interested in them sometimes.

The committee has studied this on several occasions, but we have generally had a group of the scientific community behind us to give pressure, to bring pressure, to get some of these things done.

Dr. HYNEK. I think we will see, sir, in this testimony today that you will find a corps of scientists stand ready to do this. In fact, as I mentioned in my testimony, I have private information from a very large number of scientists who are interested.

Chairman MILLER. I think this one of the values of the symposium.

As the only scientist who had been exposed to the Air Force UFO data over a twenty-year period, Dr. Hynek's testimony was impressive. He had begun his inquiries with the typical attitude that almost any intelligent person would have on hearing about the subject: the feeling that it was all "rank nonsense," as he himself terms it. But responding as would most intelligent people who viewed the evidence from an honest, objective viewpoint, he became convinced that this country, and in fact the world, is confronted with one of the most puzzling phenomena of history, regardless of the ultimate answer. (As he brought out in his testimony, it is a mistake to think that the United States has a monopoly on UFO reports.)

In sharp contrast to Dr. Condon's negative view, Dr. Hynek also finds the strong possibility of scientific value in those reports that continue to defy explanation. But the serious reliable sightings must be given *exclusive* attention, and energy must not be dissipated in examining those cases where there is even a remote possibility of the object being natural phenomena.

Dr. Hynek's statement that he restrained himself for many years, not wanting to cry "wolf," shows the caution he exercised in his early exposure to the puzzling data that continue to pour into the Air Force files. He also indicates a sharp change of attitude after the first few years. This is significant, because it might explain Dr. Condon's reluctance to give adequate credence to the many baffling cases listed as unexplainable by his own staff. If Dr. Condon engaged in UFO research over a twenty-year period as Dr. Hynek did in his official position, would he change his mind also? Further, if Dr. Condon had *personally* investigated those inexplicable cases in his own files, would he have assumed a different attitude? These are imponderable questions, but they are important because Dr. Condon's negative attitude will undoubtedly deter further scientific UFO research when it is needed most.

Dr. Hynek, it is interesting to note, also confirms Dr. Condon's own statement that perfectly sane and intelligent people are doing most of the UFO viewing, as opposed to the infinitely small percentage of lunatic-fringe sightings. Since this is mutually agreed on by the two opposing schools of thought, it remains difficult to understand why Dr. Condon fails to share Dr. Hynek's view that a continuing "detailed, conscientious, and systematic inquiry" should be urgently called for. The UFO cases involving the stopping of cars on the road, which the Condon Report acknowledges as insoluble in some cases, should, it seems, be enough to inspire Dr. Condon to at least recommend further inquiry in this area.

In stating that the public doesn't want another twenty years of confusion, Dr. Hynek hits hard at the crux of the matter, because the Colorado Report, interpreted as it was by the press, can certainly do nothing more than encourage public belief in Dr. Condon's uninformed conclusion. *Time*, for instance, implied that the Condon Report all but put to rest the entire subject of UFOs. *Newsweek* crisply stated, "A team of scientists announced that an eighteen-month study yielded no scientific evidence that UFOs were anything but natural, earthly occurrences. Not only that, the scientists also said that further extensive study of UFOs was not worth the effort." It also printed three of the most obviously unimpressive UFO photographs, one of which appears to be a meteor and the other, lenticular clouds. If these publications had made a thorough study of the Condon Report, they might not have been so easily misled by Dr. Condon's own personal opinions.

Dr. Hynek argues strongly for a "receptive scientific climate." Dr. Condon, through his conclusions, obviously seeks the exact opposite.

Two scientists of high stature thus disagree completely. But Dr. Hynek, with eighteen years more experience in examining the evidence, finds the subject "eminently worthy of study" and recommends a continuing scientific UFO board. Dr. Condon, after two years of documented apathy and disdain, seems to wish the phenomenon would go away, in opposition to the key findings of his own staff.

Dr. Hynek was only the first of the highly competent panel of scientists appearing at the hearings on July 29, most of whom took exception to Dr. Condon's negative viewpoint.

# 2.

AFTER Congressman Roush determined that there were no more questions or comment concerning Dr. Hynek's testimony, he turned to introduce Dr. James E. McDonald, the senior physicist of the Institute of Atmospheric Physics of the University of Arizona.

Dr. McDonald, a fiery, peppery man in his forties, has had a long and distinguished career as a scientist. He has been a member of the Panel on Weather and Climate Modification of the National Academy of Sciences since 1965, and his fields of special interest include atmospheric physics, physics of clouds and precipitation, meteorological optics, atmospheric electricity, and weather modification.

His interest in UFOs began only in the past few years. But impressed by the evidence he found, he has personally investigated scores of cases in various parts of the world, and has become one of the most outspoken scientists about the lag in investigating the phenomenon. His conviction is that the extraterrestrial hypothesis is the most likely.

Dr. McDonald. Thank you, Mr. Roush.

I am very pleased to have this chance to make some comments and suggestions based on my own experience to the committee, and I do wish to commend the Committee on Science and Astronautics for taking this first, and I hope very significant step, to look at the problem that has puzzled many for 20 years.

As Dr. Hynek has emphasized in his remarks, it is one of the difficulties of the problem we are talking about today that the scientific community, not just in the United States but on a world basis, has tended to discount and to regard as nonsense the UFO problem. The fact that so much anecdotal data is involved has understandably discouraged many scientists from taking seriously what, in fact, I believe is a matter of extraordinary scientific importance.

I have been studying now for about 2 years, on a rather intensive basis, the UFO problem. I have interviewed several hundred witnesses in selected cases, and I am astonished at what I have found. I had no idea that the actual UFO situation is anything like what it really appears to be.

There is a certain parallel between Dr. Hynek's slow recognition of the problem and my slow recognition of the problem. I have been curious about UFO's in a casual way for 10 or 20 years and have even checked cases in the southern Arizona area off and on rather casually, mainly encountering sincere laymen who do not recognize an aircraft strobe light, or Venus, or a bright fireball, when they see them. It is quite true that many persons misidentify natural phenomena; and my experience was mainly but not entirely limited to that sort of case.

About 2 years ago I became more than casually curious for several reasons that are not too relevant here, and began to spend much more time and very quickly changed my notions about the problem. I visited Wright-Patterson Air Force Base, saw their very impressive and surprising UFO files, the pattern of which is entirely different from what I had imagined.

At the same time, I contacted a number of private investigating UFO groups, one of the best and most constructive located here in Washington, the National Investigations

Committee on Aerial Phenomena; contacted another one of the large national groups, the Aerial Phenomenon Research Organization, and found again somewhat to my surprise, that these amateur groups operating on a shoestring basis, and frequently scorned by us scientists, were, in fact, doing really a rather good investigative job within their resources, and had compiled in their files, for instance in NICAP, on the order of 10,000 or 12,000 cases, many of which I have subsequently checked, and all of which imply a problem that has been lost from sight, swept under the rug, ignored, and now needs to be very rapidly brought out into the open as a problem demanding very serious and very high-caliber scientific attention.

I wish to emphasize that. We must very quickly have very good people looking into this problem, because it appears to be one of very serious concern. We are dealing here with inexplicable phenomena, baffling phenomena, that will not be clarified by any but the best scientists.

The scope of my remarks this morning, and the scope of my more detailed remarks in my prepared statement which has been submitted, deal with two broad areas:

I have been asked to summarize the results of my interviewing of witnesses in the last 2 years, what I found, the problems I have encountered and so on; and, secondly to address myself to the categories of past explanations of UFO sightings, that hinge on my own field of atmospheric physics.

Let me turn very briefly to my experience. In the past 2 years I have been able to devote a substantial part of my time to this problem. I have mainly concentrated on witnesses in UFO sightings that have already been checked by some of the independent groups; that is, I was no longer, in the last 2 years, dealing with original raw data where it was primarily misidentified phenomena, but rather, I was dealing with presifted, presorted data, leaning very heavily on groups like NICAP and APRO, and other groups in this country and other groups abroad for my leads and background material.

I have also had a chance to interview 75 or 80 witnesses in Australia, New Zealand, and Tasmania, when I was down in that area last summer. There were various kinds of atmospheric explanations that had been invoked in Australian cases. I must say that many of them are just as reasonable from the scientific point of view as many that we have heard in this country. But primarily I found in Austraiia that the nature of the sightings is similar to those in the United States, disc-like objects, cigar-shaped objects, objects without wings, without evident means of propulsion, frequently hovering without any sound, sometimes making sounds, hovering over cars, stopping cars, as Dr. Hynek has pointed out, causing interference with the ignition system, and the same kind of public reluctance to report was very evident.

I want to emphasize, as one of the very important misconceptions that has been fostered, that instead of dealing with witnesses who are primarily looking for notoriety, who want to tell a good story, who are all out to gain attention, it is generally quite the opposite. And this is true in Australia, too. People are quite unwilling to tell you about a UFO sighting, afraid acquaintances would think they have "gone around the bend," as Australians put it. Over and over you encounter that. People are reluctant to report what they are seeing. There is a real ridicule lid that has not been contrived by any group, it just has evolved in the way the whole problem has unfolded. This is not entirely new in science. It has occurred before.

I am sure a number here at the speakers' table are familiar with an interesting chapter in science years ago when meteorites, out of which NASA and many scientists around the world now get a very large amount of useful scientific information, were scorned and scoffed as unreal. It was regarded as nonsense that peasants were telling stories about stones falling out of the sky. The efforts of a few scientists to take a look at the problem and to get some initial data simply were ignored until a very unusual but very real event occurred in northern France, a meteorite shower. So they sent an eminent academician out to have a look at what these people were talking about, and by golly, the peasants appeared to be right. Everybody in the village, the prefect of police, the local administrators, all the peasants, had seen stones fall out of the sky, and for the first time the French Academy deigned to take a look at the problem. Meteoritics was born.

Here we now face a very similar situation in science. We have tended to ignore it because we didn't think it made sense. It definitely defies any explanation, and hence the situation has evolved where we can't get going because we aren't already going.

The scientific community as a whole won't take this problem seriously because it doesn't have scientific data. They want instrumental data.

Why don't they have instrumental data? Because the scientists don't take it seriously enough to get the scientific data. It is like the 20-year-old who can't get a job because he lacks experience, and he lacks experience because he hasn't had a job. In the same way you find the scientist wishing you would give him good hard meter readings and magnetometer traces, and so on, but we don't have it yet because the collective body of scientists, including myself, have ignored UFO's.

Turning to some of the highlights of my interviewing experience, I first mention the "ridicule lid." We are not dealing with publicity seekers. We are not, and I here concur with Dr. Hynek's remarks, we are not dealing with religiosity and cultism. Those persons aren't really the least bit interested in observations. They have firm convictions entirely independent of observations. They do not cause noise that disturbs the real signal at all.

General Samford of the Air Force put it well, 16 years ago. General Samford, then Director of Intelligence, said, and I would concur 100 percent, "Credible observers are observing relatively incredible objects." That was said 16 years ago, and it is still occurring.

I will touch in a moment or two on a sighting in Mr. Pettis' district that very well illustrates that, a sighting this year in Redlands, Calif., which I think Dr. Harder may be able to tell still more about.

Another characteristic in interviewing the witnesses is the tendency for the UFO witness to turn first not to the hypothesis that he is looking at a spaceship, but rather it must be an ambulance out there with a blinking red light or that it is a helicopter up there. There is a conventional interpretation considered first; only then does the witness get out of the car or patrol car and realize the thing is stopped in midair and is going backwards and has six bright lights, or something like that. Only after an economical first hypothesis does the witness, in these impressive cases, go further in his hypothesis, and finally realize he is looking at something he has never seen before.

I like Dr. Hynek's phrase for this, "escalation of hypotheses." This tendency to take a simple guess first and then upgrade it is so characteristic that I emphasize it as a very important point.

Then, looking at the negative side, all of us who have checked cases are sometimes in near anguish at the typical inability of the scientifically untrained person to estimate angles, to even understand what you are asking for when you ask for an angular estimation. We are all aware of the gross errors in distances, heights, and speeds so estimated.

And I would emphasize to those who cite jury trial experience that the tendency for a group of witnesses to an accident to come in with quite different accounts, must not be overstressed here. Those witnesses don't come in from, say, a street corner accident and claim they saw a giraffe killed by a tiger. They talk about an accident. They are confused about details. There is legally confusing difference of timing and distance, and so on; but all are in agreement that it was an auto accident.

So also when you deal with multiple-witness cases in UFO sightings. There is an impressive core of consistency; everybody is talking about an object that has no wings, all of 10 people may say it was dome shaped or something like that, and then there are minor differences as to how they thought it was, how far away, and so on. Those latter variations do pose a very real problem. It stands as a negative factor with respect to the anecdotal data, but it does not mean we are not dealing with real sightings of real objects.

Then there is the very real but not terribly serious problem of the hoaxes, fabricators, liars, and so on. You do encounter cases from time to time where you end up thinking, well, this person has some reason to have invented the whole story. Sometimes it is fairly apparent. Sometimes it takes a lot of digging to prove it.

I might say here that the independent investigative groups have done an excellent job. It takes a knowledge of human characteristics, not scientific expertise to detect lies and hoaxes.

Then there is the problem that you always have to be sure in talking with witnesses that you are not dealing with somebody already very enthusiastic about UFO's. You have to try to establish, and this is not always easy, whether he has prior knowledge of the whole UFO literature. Are you dealing with somebody who is just telling you again what he has read in a recent magazine in the barber chair?

I emphasize that my experience is that again and again

you find people who were not really interested in UFO's until they saw one themselves. Then they suddenly became very, very concerned, as one more member of the public who has become a UFO witness; and in this body of citizens there are some very distressed persons who wish that the scientific community, or the Government, were doing something about this problem.

The types of objects that are being seen, and I state the word "objects" not "hazy lights," are spread over quite a range of types, a baffling range.

I want to use that word many times, because it speaks for my experience. The UFO problem is baffling. But there is a predominance of disc-shaped objects and elongated cigar-shaped objects, objects without wings, appendages, tails, and that sort of thing. Typically, wingless objects, disc- and cigar-shaped.

The same type of observations have been coming from all parts of the world, and have been for a number of years. My direct interviews with a witness in Australia speak for that global pattern.

Another characteristic that emerges is a quite fluctuatory frequency of sightings. Right now, in the past few months, there have not been very many really impressive cases that have come up; but last fall, for example, England had a wave of sightings which were unprecedented in the English experience, that led, for example, to a BBC documentary that has just been produced. It led also to a recently published study, that I got only a couple of weeks ago from the Stoke-on-Trent area in Staffordshire, 70 sightings in about a 2½-month period in this area. It happens that one of my colleagues is an English physicist from that very area. As he points out, these are no-nonsense people who are not airy-fairy types that would be on LSD, or seeing ghosts in the sky.

He is puzzled, and I am puzzled.

Well, there are many questions that are asked by skeptical scientists, skeptical members of the public; and skepticism, as Mark Twain said, is what gets you an education.

There are questions like, "Why aren't UFO's seen abroad?" "Why aren't UFO's seen by airline pilots?" "Why aren't UFO's seen by crowds of people rather than by lone individuals?" "Why aren't they tracked by radar?" "Why don't weather observers and meteorologists see UFO's?"

"Why aren't there sonic booms, or why aren't there crashed UFO's?"

Finally, a very frequently raised question, "If the UFO's are from somewhere else, if they are really devices that represent some high civilization, why no contact?" This is a question that comes up again and again, since most persons who know enough about the UFO problem to realize there must be something there, cannot, in their first view of the problem, visualize a visitation from elsewhere, surveillance, or what have you, without contact.

I want to return to that point later, but I wish to emphasize that that is a fallacious question. If we were under surveillance from some advanced technology sufficiently advanced to do what we cannot do in the sense of interstellar travel, then, as Arthur Clarke has put it quite well, quoted in *Time* magazine the last week, we have an odd situation. Arthur Clarke points out that any sufficiently advanced technology would be indistinguishable from magic. How well that applies to UFO sightings. You have a feeling you are dealing with some very high technology, devices of an entirely real nature which defy explanation in terms of present-day science. To say that we could anticipate the values, reasons, motivations, and so on, of any such system that has the capability of getting here from somewhere else is fallacious.

That is a homocentric fallacy of the most obvious nature, yet it is asked over and over again.

In my prepared statement I will be able to cover more of these points, of course.

The heart of the problem lies in citing cases, and I have investigated, personally, on the order of 300 cases dealing with key witnesses. I have looked as carefully as I can for all reasonable explanations.

There are many cases that fall apart when you investigate them. Then there are far too many that resist the best analysis that many of us have been able to subject them to.

Let me just cite briefly, to take a recent case rather than an old one, the instance at Redlands, and perhaps Dr. Harder can fill you in in more detail.

On February 4 of this year, at 7:20 in the evening, over a residential area in that city of population 30,000, a disc was seen. Twenty witnesses interviewed by University of Redlands' investigators, described it as having "windows" or "ports" or something of that sort. They interviewed a little over half a dozen of them and all saw something on the bottom that they described as "looking like jets."

This object was hovering at an estimated height of about 300 feet. The estimates vary, but it came out about 300 feet. The citizens had gone out in the street because dogs were barking and, because they had heard an unusual noise, and pretty soon there were people all up and down the street. It was estimated that more than 100 witnesses were involved, and 20 were directly interviewed.

Here was an object seen by many persons. It hovered, then shot up to about double the height, hovered again, and moved down across Redlands a short distance, hovered once again, and then took off rapidly to the northwest.

This case has not received any scientific attention beyond this investigation by Dr. Philip Seff and his colleagues. It has not received public notoriety. This was, in fact, only reported in a short column in the local paper and not on the wires anywhere. That happens over and over again.

Here, for example, are the reports for one month of last fall, clipping-service coverage on the things that get local coverage, but don't get on the wires, because in the present climate of the opinion, wire editors, like scientists, Congressmen, and the public at large, feel sure there is nothing to all this, and they don't put them on the wires. You have to go right to the local town to get press coverage in most cases.

The Redlands, February 1968, case illustrates that very well. Once in a while a case will get on the wires and receive national attention, but by and large, one just doesn't read about these cases in other parts of the country, because wire services don't carry them.

Let me tell you another case that answers the questions: "Why aren't there multiple witnesses?" "Why aren't they seen in cities?" "Why aren't these ever seen in the daytime?"

It is true that there is a preponderance of nighttime sights. Maybe this is merely a matter of luminosity.

It is also true that there seem to be more reports from rather remote areas, say desert areas or swampy areas, than in the middle of cities. But there are city observations. And it is also true there are more individual witness cases than sightings by large crowds. But in every instance there are striking exceptions to this.

In New York City, on November 22, 1966, a total of eight witnesses, members of the staff of the American Newspaper Publishers Association, were the witnesses in a good case. I interviewed William Leick, of that staff, the manager of the office there. I heard about it through a NICAP report. It did not appear in the papers, as I will mention. William Leick had been looking out the window, saw an object over the U.N. building. It was hovering, and as he talked to a colleague he realized there was something odd about it, so they walked out on the terrace. Soon they had six others out on the terrace. This was at 4:30 in the afternoon. It was kind of a cushion-shaped object, as he described it, and had no wings. It was rocking a little from time to time, blinked in the afternoon sun a little bit, had kind of an orange glow. All eight were watching, and after it hovered for several moments it rose vertically and then took off at high speed. There is an example of midtown sighting in New York where the witnesses are staff members of a responsible organization. Leick, himself, had been trained in intelligence, in World War II. There is no reason at all to think he and his colleagues would invent this.

They did call a New York paper, but to say they weren't the least bit interested. There was no report published in a New York paper. Next they called a local Air Force office but no one came to investigate it. It came to my attention because one of the members of the staff knew of NICAP and sent NICAP a report.

This sort of thing has happened over and over again. The ridicule lid keeps these out of sight; too many of them are occurring to delay any longer in getting at this problem with all possible scientific assistance.

A famous multiple-witness instance occurred in Farmington, N. Mex., on March 17, 1950. I interviewed seven witnesses there. A very large number of objects were involved. There were several different groups of objects, all described as disc-shaped objects. They were explained as Skyhook balloons, officially, so I checked into that.

I finally established that there was no Skyhook balloon released anywhere in the United States on or near that day. The witnesses included some of the leading citizens in the town. It was reported nationally at that time but was soon forgotten.

I have interviewed one of the witnesses in a Washington State sighting, at Longview, Wash., July 3, 1949. An air show was being held and someone spotted the UFO because there was a sky-writing aircraft overhead that some people were watching. They spotted the first of three disc-like objects that came over Longview that morning. The person whom I interviewed is a former Navy commander, Moulton B. Taylor. He was the manager of the air show, so he got on the public address system and got everybody to look at this object before it crossed the skies. It was fluttering as it went across the sky. There were pilots, engineers, police officers, and Longview residents in the audience. Many had binoculars. Taylor estimated it to be about 10 minutes of arc in diameter. Because the aircraft was still skywriting people continued to watch the sky. Two successive objects of the same type flew over in the next 20 minutes. A total of three objects came over, and they were from three different directions: one from the north, one from the northwest, and one almost from the west, quite clearly ruling out an explanation like balloons, which became the official explanation. There were no balloon stations anywhere near Longview, Wash., as a matter of fact, and the balloon explanation is quite inadequate.

Here we have a case of over a hundred witnesses to the passage of a wingless object moving at relatively high velocity. When the second and third objects went over, someone had the presence of mind to time the fluttering rate—it was 48 per minute.

Here again we have a multiple-witness case, a daytime sighting case, and one which you can't quickly write off.

If time permitted I would talk about a number of radar cases. One of the most famous is the Washington National Airport sighting. On July 19, 1952, CAA radars and Andrews Air Force radars tracked unknowns moving at variable speeds from 100 miles an hour to over 800 miles an hour, and a number of airline pilots in the air saw these, and were in some instances vectored in by the CAA radar people, and then saw luminous objects in the same area that they showed on radar up near Herndon and Martinsburg.

I talked to five of these CAA people. One can still go back and check these old cases, I emphasize. I also talked to four of the airline pilots who were in the air at the time. I have gone over the quantitative aspects of the official explanation that this was ducting or trapping of the radar beams. That is quite untenable. I have gone over the radiosonde, computed the radar refractive index gradient, and it is nowhere near the ducting gradient.

Also, it is very important that at one time three different radars, two CAA and one Andrews Air Force Base radar, all got compatible echoes. That is extremely significant.

And finally from a radar-propagation point of view, the angles of propagation, radar and visual, were far above any values that would permit trapping, which makes this a case which is not an explained case. It was an instance of unidentified aerial objects over our Capital, I believe.

One could go on with many cases. I want to just briefly touch two categories of atmospheric explanations that have been rather widely discussed, and close with that.

Meteorological optics is a subject that I enjoy and have looked into over the years rather carefully, and I must express for the record my very strong disagreement with Dr. Donald H. Menzel, former director of Harvard Observatory, whose two books on the subject of UFO's lean primarily on meteorological explanations. I have checked case after case of his, and his explanations are very, very far removed from what are well-known principles and quantitative aspects of meteorological optic objects. He has made statements that simply do not fit what is known about meteorological objects.

I would be prepared to talk all day on specific illustrations but time will not permit more.

Secondly, there has more recently been a suggestion made by "Aviation Week" Senior Editor Philip J. Klass, that the really interesting UFO's are atmospheric-electrical plasmas of some type similar to ball lightning, but perhaps something different, something we don't yet understand but are generated by atmospheric processes.

The first time anyone tried the ball lightning hypothesis was in Air Force Project Grudge, back in 1949. The Weather Bureau was asked to do a special study of ball lightning. I recently got a declassified copy of that, and the Air Force position at that time, and since then was that ball lightning doesn't come near to explaining these sightings. I concur in that. When you deal with multiple-witness cases involving discs with metallic luster, definite outline, seen in the daytime, completely removed from a thunderstorm, perhaps seen over center Manhattan, or perhaps in Redlands, Calif., they are not ball lightning or plasmas.

In weather completely unrelated to anything that could provide a source of energy, the continuous power source required to maintain a plasma in the face of recombination and decay of a plasma, Klass' views just do not make good sense.

It is just not reasonable to suggest that, say the BOAC Stratocruiser that was followed by six UFO's for 90 miles up in the St. Lawrence Valley in 1954 was followed by a plasma, or that these people in Redlands were looking at a plasma, or that the 20 or so objects that went over Farmington were plasmas.

One of the most characteristic features of a plasma is its very short lifetime and exceedingly great instability, as some of your members will know from your contact with fusion research problems. The difficulty of sustaining a plasma for more than microseconds is a very great difficulty. To suggest that clear weather conditions can somehow create and maintain plasmas that persist for many minutes, and fool pilots with 18,000 flight hours into thinking that they are white- and red-domed discs, to take a very famous case over Philadelphia where the pilot thought he was about 100 yards from this dome-disc, is unreasonable. It is not a scientifically well-defended viewpoint.

To conclude, then, my position is that UFO's are entirely real and we do not know what they are, because we have laughed them out of court. The possibility that these are extraterrestrial devices, that we are dealing with surveillance from some advanced technology, is a possibility I take very seriously.

I reach that hypothesis, as my preferred hypothesis, not by hard fact, hardware, tailfins, or reading license plates, but by having examined hundreds of cases and rejected the alternative hypothesis as capable of accounting for them.

I am afraid that this possibility has sufficiently good backing for it, despite its low a priori ability, that we must examine it. I think your committee, with its many concerns for the entire aerospace program, as well as our whole national scientific program, has a very special reason for examining that possibility. Should that possibility be correct, if there is even a chance of its being correct, we ought to get our best people looking at it. Instead, we are collectively laughing at this possibility.

To meet Mr. Rumsfeld's request, let me remark on Dr. Hynek's two recommendations. I strongly concur in the need for some new approach. I am sure Dr. Hynek was not suggesting there be one single UFO committee. In fact, he said, "not a one-shot approach." A pluralistic approach to the problem is needed here.

The Defense Department is already supporting some work on it. NASA definitely has a need to look at this problem. We have to pay very serious attention to the problem and get a variety of new approaches.

The other point Dr. Hynek mentioned was that we try to look at this on a worldwide basis. This is crucially important. We are dealing with a real problem here, and I insist it is a global problem. We can study it in the United States, but if we ignore what is happening in France and England—one of the greatest UFO waves that ever occurred was in France—would be a serious mistake. I strongly urge that your committee consider holding rather more extensive hearings in which a larger segment of the scientific community is given the opportunity to talk pro and con on the issue, hearings aimed at getting a new measure of scientific attention to this important problem.

Thank you.

Mr. ROUSH. Thank you, Dr. McDonald, for your presentation.

As we explained awhile ago, we are pressed for time. We are entertaining questions from members of the committee.

Mr. Bell.

Mr. BELL. Dr. McDonald, I want to compliment you on your interesting statement. But what leads you to believe that whatever these phenomena are, they are extraterrestrial?

What facts do you have?

Dr. McDONALD. May I say I wouldn't use the word "believe." I would say the "hypothesis" that these are extraterrestrial surveillance, is the hypothesis I presently regard as most likely.

As I mentioned, it is not hard facts in the sense of irrefutable proof, but dealing with case after case wherein the witnesses showed credibility I can't impugn. That impresses me. These are not at all like geophysical or astronomical phenomena; they appear to be craft-like machine-like devices. I would have to answer you in terms of case after case that I and others have investigated, to make all this clear. It is this very large body of impressive witnesses' testimony, radar-tracking data on ultra-high-speed objects sometimes moving at over 5,000 miles an hour, UFO's, combined radar-visual sightings, and just too much other consistent evidence that suggests we are dealing with machine-like devices from somewhere else.

Mr. BELL. Have there been pictures taken?

Dr. McDONALD. Yes; there have been pictures taken.

For instance, a photograph taken in Ohio, by an Air Force photo reconnaissance plane May 24, 1954. I recently have looked a little more closely at the data. This was explained as an undersun, but that idea is subject to quantitative observation. The angles just do not fit. There is a very important case at Edwards Air Force base with two witnesses, where they got photographs of the object. Unfortunately, in this case I have not seen the photo, but I have talked with the persons who took it. There are photographs, but not nearly as many as we would like. We would like to have lots of them. In a case in Corning, Calif., a police officer, one of five witnesses, had a loaded camera in his patrol car, 20 paces from where he watched the object, didn't even think of getting his camera. He said he was too flabbergasted to think of it. That is a part of the problem.

Mr. ROUSH. Mr. Hechler.

Mr. HECHLER. Have you examined any reports of communication by these objects?

Dr. McDONALD. Yes; the problem of contact is very important. There is one category of contact, not in the sense of shaking hands, but rather light response. I have a file on several of these, and I'm looking for more. For instance, in Shamokin, Pa., Kerstetter is the name of the witness, he works for a bank in Shamokin. I talked to the president of the bank as to his reliability and got very good recommendations. Last year, he and his wife and family were in a car near a mountain ridge in Shamokin, saw a thing hovering over the mountain, like the flashing lights of a theater marquee. He had a flashlight. He didn't know Morse code, but it really didn't matter. He sent light flashes in various orders and he got lights back from the thing. That same thing happened in Newton, N.H., in August of last year, where several persons saw an object coming overhead. The same thought occurred to them and they signaled with a flashlight. It wasn't Morse, it was dot dash dot, then dash dash dash, and it came back with no failure, replicated light signals. The same thing happened in West Virginia, where a pharmacist, named Sommers, did it with his headlights. When I was in Australia, I talked about some hunters out hunting kangaroo. A disc came over, one said "give them Morse"; the flash came back faithfully, and they left in a hurry. Is that contact? I don't know. Nobody got any intelligence out of it either way, if you will pardon the whimsy. It would be terrible if in fact this was surveillance and our technology was represented by the Eveready flashlight. [Laughter.]

We may be flunking our exam.

Mr. ROUSH. Mr. Downing.

Mr. DOWNING. I'm interested in your testimony. On page 10 of your written statement, you say it is unfortunate no acceptable version of Reference 6 exists, though it has managed to get it into the status of limited acceptability.

Why is this not available?

Dr. McDONALD. Well, that was an Air Force document. This was completed in 1949. These were classified until just a few years back. No one could get access to them, because they were under DOD classification. But the 12-year rule expired, and Dr. Leon Davidson managed to get a copy.

It is accessible in the sense that if I want to pay $90 for Xeroxes I can now get it. It is not published in the sense of being available to every library in the country. My Reference 7, which NICAP just published, is available to scientists all over the country. It is a matter of the Air Force having a policy of not publishing such items, and they were classified. I think the Moss committee and NICAP are to be highly praised to get out in the open Reference 7.

Mr. DOWNING. Is there a reason why this is classified?

Dr. MCDONALD. There is an understandable reason why the Air Force has had to classify this. An unidentified area object on presumption is hostile until proved otherwise. So there has been this unfortunate, but entirely understandable measuring of these two areas. The national defense mission of the Air Force has necessitated they have some part of the UFO problem inevitably, and they got it in the first instance. They have long since told us there is no hostility here, hence the scientific curiosities going unattended because it doesn't fall under the defense mission, in other words to be transferred into NASA, NSF, or something like that. That does not mean the Air Force won't continue to watch unidentified objects on the millisecond basis. But they not need worry about this other part of the problem. I think it is understandable, but needs changing.

Mr. ROUSH. Mr. Pettis.

Mr. PETTIS. Mr. Chairman, Doctor.

I was a little bit interested in your observations about this UFO sighting in my hometown of Redlands.

I might observe that Redlands is a rather conservative community, when people in Redlands say they saw something, they saw something. I did not happen to be in Redlands that particular date, so I did not see this.

But I would like to observe this, that having spent a great deal of my life in the air, as a pilot, professional and private pilot, I know that many pilots and professional pilots have seen phenomena that they could not explain.

These men, most of whom have talked to me, have been very reticent to talk about this publicly, because of the ridicule that they were afraid would be heaped upon them, and I'm sure that if this committee were ever to investigate this, or bring them in here, there probably would have to be a closed hearing, Mr. Chairman.

However, there is a phenomena [*sic*] here that isn't explained.

I think probably we ought to do a little looking into this, is my personal opinion.

Mr. ROUSH. Mr. Ryan.

Mr. RYAN. Yes, thank you, Mr. Chairman.

First I should like to commend you, Mr. Roush, for your interest in the subject matter, and the chairman of the full committee for having arranged for hearings into this problem.

I think it is important that this committee not waive its jurisdiction, but that it explore very carefully the proposals that have been made by the witnesses here, and that it have a continuing field of exploration into this whole question. I want to commend Dr. McDonald for having been persistent in presenting his views to the various members of the committee, helping to bring about these hearings.

I wondered, Dr. McDonald, if you would care to evaluate the research project at the University of Colorado, and comment on that?

Mr. ROUSH. Mr. Ryan, may I just say we had agreed that this was not the place to discuss that particular project, and that the purpose of the symposium was not to go into the activities of another branch of government, but rather to explore that as a scientific phenomena [*sic*].

I'm sure that Dr. McDonald would be very happy to confer with you privately on this, but if you could show some restraint here, the Chair would be real grateful to you.

Mr. RYAN. Well, let me rephrase my question.

In view of the fact that there has been a study conducted by a project in the Air Force, and the University of Colorado, do you believe there is anything further that should be done by any branch of the Government?

Dr. McDONALD. Emphatically, yes.

Mr. RYAN. What would you recommend?

Dr. McDONALD. I think that we need to get a much broader basis of investigation of UFO's, as I did say, a few moments ago, it would be very salutary to have a group in NASA looking at this problem, and to have some NASA support of independent studies. It would be very good for the National Science Foundation to support, say, some university people interested in it. It would be good to have the Office of Naval Research et cetera involved.

We don't deal with many other important problems, space, or molecular biology or health without a pluralistic approach, a multiplicity of research programs. I don't want to touch a frayed nerve here. This problem of duplication is sometimes lamented. But by and large I think you will agree we would gain from having a lot of different people with slightly different points of view going at every problem. At the moment everything is focused through one agency, and everything now hinges on that one particular program you have asked me about, and my answer was, we very definitely need some independent programs.

I am on record elsewhere than here in my specific views on that project.

Mr. RYAN. Looking back at page 14, you wrote a letter to the National Academy of Sciences, concerning this project. Have you had any reaction from the National Academy of Sciences?

Dr. McDONALD. Yes, I received a letter from Dr. Seitz, saying for the time being we must let the Colorado project run its course. That was the gist of the answer.

Mr. ROUSH. I would appreciate it, if we dispensed with that. Let me say that the National Academy is undertaking an evaluation of the University of Colorado project, and this will be published.

Mr. RYAN. I'm suggesting maybe this committee should make an investigation of the University of Colorado project.

Chairman MILLER. That is something we don't have authority to do here.

Mr. RYAN. To what extent, Dr. McDonald, have sightings been picked up by radar, and what extent of those that have been picked up been explored?

Dr. McDONALD. Well, there are many such sightings, I dare say there are thousands of military radar sightings that were for the short period unidentified. Then they identify them. But here is an impressive number of both military and civilian radar sightings that defy radar explanation in terms of unknown phenomena. Most of these deficiencies are well understood, so one can be fairly sure that many of these unidentified radar cases have no conventional explanation.

In a case where a P-61 flew over Japan, back some years ago, made six passes at an unidentified object it was getting radar returns on, and the pilot saw it visually. Here you are dealing with an unknown. Then there was a case in Michigan where a ground radar detected an object at 600 miles an hour coming in over Saginaw Bay. The pilot got a radar return, and also saw a vast luminous object; the object turned in a very sharp 180-degree turn and went back, and eluded the F-94. Here you are dealing wtih a case where radar propagation anomalies will not explain it. There was one radar in the airplane at 20,000 feet and one radar on the ground, both showing the object. There are many cases like that which I could enlarge on.

Mr. RYAN. Let me ask a further question: In the course of your investigation and your study of UFO sightings, have you found any cases where contemporaneously with the sighting of UFO's allegedly, there were any other events which took place, which might or might not be related to the UFO's?

Dr. McDONALD. Yes. Certainly there are many physical effects. For instance, in Mr. Pettis' district, several people found the fillings in their mouth hurting while this object was nearby, but there are many cases probably on record of car ignition failure. One famous case was at Levelland, Tex., in 1967. Ten vehicles were stopped within a short area, all independently in a 2-hour period, near Levelland, Tex. There was no lightning or thunder storm, and only a trace of rain. There is another which I don't know whether to bring to the committee's attention or not. The evidence is not as conclusive as the car stopping phenomenon, but there are too many instances for me to ignore. UFO's have often been seen hovering near power facilities. There are a small number but still a little too many to seem pure fortuitous chance, of system outages, coincident with the UFO sighting. One of the cases was Tamaroa, Ill. Another was a case in Shelbyville, Ky., early last year. Even the famous one, the New York blackout, involved UFO sightings. Dr. Hynek probably would be the most appropriate man to describe the Manhattan sighting, since he interviewed several witnesses involved. I interviewed a woman in Seacliff, N.Y. She saw a disk hovering and going up and down. And then shooting away from New York just after the power failure. I went to the FPC for data, they didn't take them seriously although they had many dozens of sighting reports for that famous evening. There were reports all over New England in the midst of that blackout, and five witnesses near Syracuse, N.Y., saw a glowing object ascending within about a minute of the blackout. First they thought it was a dump burning right at the moment the lights went out. It is rather puzzling that the pulse of current that tripped the relay at the Ontario Hydro Commission plant has never been identified, but initially the tentative suspicion was centered on the Clay Substation of the Niagara Mohawk network right there in the Syracuse area, where unidentified aerial phenomenon has been seen by some of the witnesses.

This extends down to the limit of single houses losing their power when a UFO is near. The hypothesis in the case of car stopping is that there might be high magnetic fields, d.c. fields, which saturate the core and thus prevent the pulses going through the system to the other side. Just how a UFO could trigger an outage on a large power network is however not yet clear. But this is a disturbing series of coincidences that I think warrant much more attention than they have so far received.

Mr. RYAN. As far as you know, has any agency investigated the New York blackout in relation to UFO?

Dr. McDONALD. None at all. When I spoke to the FPC people, I was dissatisfied with the amount of information I could gain. I am saying there is a puzzling and slightly disturbing coincidence here. I'm not going on record as saying, yes, these are clear-cut cause and effect relations. I'm saying it ought to be looked at. There is no one looking at this relation between UFO's and outages.

Mr. ROUSH. Our time is really running short, Mr. Ryan.

Mr. RYAN. One final question. Do you think it is imperative that the Federal Power Commission, or Federal Communications Commission, investigate the relation if any between the sightings and the blackout?

Dr. McDONALD. My position would call for a somewhat weaker adjective. I'd say extremely desirable.

Mr. ROUSH. Thank you.

Thank you, Dr. McDonald.


Dr. McDonald's testimony is noteworthy because of its directness and force. He considers the extraterrestrial hypothesis the most likely explanation of the phenomena. On examining the *best* UFO evidence, it is certainly possible to rule out practically every other hypothesis, and it is on this basis that Dr. McDonald and others lean toward the theory that we are undergoing surveillance from intelligently guided craft from extraterrestrial sources. No intelligent observer, however, would make a dogmatic statement on this premise.

Like Dr. Hynek, Dr. McDonald was slow to acknowledge the mounting seriousness of UFO evidence. When he did turn his attention to it, like many others he found it much more solid than what he had imagined. His attitude again brings up the question as to whether Dr. Condon would not undergo the same metamorphosis if he continued to probe the subject.

Because of the baffling nature of the phenomena, Dr. McDonald calls for the conscientious attention of our best scientists. He explains the lack of hard instrumentation data as being due to the fact that scientists have not taken the subject seriously. And the Colorado study certainly did not allow enough time to set such an instrumentation study up correctly.

McDonald confirms several premises brought up by Dr. Hynek in his previous testimony: the puzzle of the car ignition cases as documented by multiple witnesses, the severe "ridicule lid" that prevents many responsible people from reporting their sightings, the comparison to the attitude of the scientific establishment before meteorites were confirmed, the fact that we are dealing with thousands—if not millions—of reliable witnesses rather than cultists, the fact that most people are indifferent until they encounter a sighting themselves, and the many misconceptions people have about the subject because of misinformation by the press. This misinformation will certainly be increased by the negative conclusions reached by Dr. Condon in spite of the buried positive material within his own report.

The attention Dr. McDonald pays to the negative findings of Dr. Menzel is most interesting. As a meteorologist, McDonald finds that Menzel hasn't done very good homework in slipping from astronomy into this field. The same is true with the theories of Philip Klass, who attempted to explain away UFO sightings as plasma or ball lightning. As McDonald points out, even the Air Force agrees that Klass's theory is untenable, especially in the light of the micro-second lifetime of these phenomena.

Congressman William Ryan's inquiries about the then-pending Condon report are most interesting, and it is some-what regrettable that the ground rules of the hearings did not permit an open assessment of Condon's project. Ryan called for an investigation of the Colorado project, and in the light of Condon's conclusions in the face of his own evidence, this step would certainly not seem out of order.

McDonald's personal opinion of the Colorado study is well-documented. His statements elsewhere indicate that he feels that the study was conducted under leadership of extreme bias, that Dr. Condon made little effort to person-ally investigate significant cases, that the famous "trick" memo by Robert Low reflected the entire spirit of the lead-ership of the study.

The prepared statement of Dr. McDonald that was read into the record of the hearings is a masterpiece of documen-tation and detail. It occupies some fifty pages of small type in the official records, and examines every phase of the UFO problem in cold, logical, scientific terms. Even a skeptic, if he took the time to read this material thoroughly, could not help but be impressed.

In the written statement for the Congressional committee, Dr. McDonald tells how he began by directly interview-ing key witnesses, and as a result, he says, "I rapidly altered my conception of the scientific importance of the UFO ques-tion." He became acutely concerned with the neglect of the subject. He attributes this neglect to the preconceptions that block serious consideration of the problem. He grants that UFOs are a highly unconventional problem, and that their elusive, unpredictable patterns make them extremely difficult to assess scientifically.

He lists eight principal hypotheses, which he uses as a yardstick to appraise the high-quality type of report:

1. Hoaxes, fabrications, and frauds
2. Hallucinations, mass hysteria, rumor phenomena
3. Lay misinterpretations of well-known physical phenomena (meteorological, astronomical, optical, aeronautical, etc.)
4. Semi-secret advance technology (new test vehicles, satellites, novel weapons, flares, re-entry phenomena, etc.)
5. Poorly understood physical phenomena (rare atmospheric-electrical or other effects, unusual meteoric phenomena, natural or artificial plasmoids, etc.)
6. Poorly understood psychological phenomena
7. Extraterrestrial devices of some surveillance nature
8. Spaceships bringing messengers of terrestrial salvation and occult truth

The last postulate he of course brushes off, but it must be listed to keep the theories complete. Further, it is the people who do embrace this occult theory who have discouraged scientific interest in the genuinely documented technical evidence. As such, the last theory plays an important *negative* role in blocking further study. "A disturbing number of prominent scientists," Dr. McDonald writes, "have jumped off all too easily, to the conclusion that only the nuts see UFOs."

In analyzing the other seven points, Dr. McDonald indicates that the first six can account for a good percentage of the sightings. Hoaxes do crop up, but they are a small percentage of the reports, and can be easily eliminated by an intelligent analyst. Mass hysteria can frequently cause misinterpretation of phenomena, but this in turn is not difficult to screen out by careful investigation, and such cases have no bearing on the cases McDonald personally investigated. Misinterpretations of natural phenomena also occur, but by no means does this hypothesis cover all UFO cases, as some unfamiliar with the total technical evidence are led to believe. Semi-secret experiments cannot be taken as a total explanation in view of the many years of observation, the worldwide sightings involving gross and constant violation of international air space, and numerous violations of FAA regulations for craft over populated areas. "Almost no one any longer seriously proposes that the truly puzzling UFO reports of close range sighting of what appear to be machines of some sort are chance sightings of secret test devices (ours or theirs)," Dr. McDonald writes. He goes on to give the atmospheric ball-lightning type of case little credence when he says that this theory would "hold some weight if it were true that we dealt therein only with reports of hazy, glowing masses comparable to, say, ball lightning or if we dealt only with fast-moving luminous bodies moving across the sky in meteoric fashion."

Going to the sixth theory, even psychologists grant that the entire mass of the phenomena could not possibly be explained by psychological aberrations, especially in view of the radar trackings, the effect on auto ignitions, the effect on animals, and competent technical witness testimony.

Because no single hypothesis can stand up under full scrutiny of the evidence, Dr. McDonald finally draws the conclusion that the most likely is the seventh, the extra-terrestrial-surveillance theory. After pointing out that official assurances of careful investigation were falsely being circulated, he writes:

Hypothesis Number 7 has thus received short shrift from science to date. As one scientist who has gone to some effort to try to examine the facts, I say that this has been an egregious, if basically unwitting, scientific error—an error that must be rectified with a minimum of further delay. On the basis of the evidence I have examined, and on the basis of my own weighing of alternative hypotheses (including some not listed), I now regard Hypothesis 7 as the one more likely to prove correct. My scientific instincts lead me to hedge that prediction just to the extent of suggesting that if the UFOs are not of extramundane origin, then I suspect that they will prove to be something very much more bizarre, something of perhaps even greater scientific interest than extraterrestrial devices.

In the many pages of his written report, Dr. McDonald spells out the steps that led him to his conclusion on a case-by-case basis. He lists in detail eight cases of airline crew sightings to document the misconception that pilots don't report UFO sightings. He lists in detail some seven cases to show a representative sample of multiple-witness sightings. He goes into intricate detail on five cases over large urban centers, including the sighting by eight employees of the American Newspaper Publishers Association in Manhattan. He examines in detail six sightings by astronomers, five by meteorologists and weather observers. He shows how four major sightings attributed to weather balloons could not possibly have fallen in this classification. Three cases involving photographs investigated personally by Dr. McDonald are recorded, including one at Edwards Air Force Base that was felt by one member of the University of Colorado study to be an extremely significant case.

Physical effects and car-stopping cases and other electromagnetic effects are given full attention, based on his own direct investigation in the field.

In his own specialty as an atmospheric physicist, he challenges the theories of Menzel.

In my opinion, we cannot explain away UFOs on either meteorological or astronomical grounds. . . . A principal diffi-

culty with Menzel's mirage explanations is that he typically over-
looks completely stringent quantitative restrictions on the angle
of elevation of the observer's line of sight in mirage effects. . . .
In Menzel's explanations and in certain of the official explanations . . . mirages are involved to account for UFOs when the
observer's line of sight may depart from the horizontal by as
much as five to ten degrees or even more. I emphasize that this
is entirely unreasonable. . . . Some of the most interesting UFOs
have been seen at close range directly overhead, quite obviously
ruling out mirage explanations.

As far as Klass's ball-lightning and plasma theories are
concerned, Dr. McDonald comments:

One phenomenon in the area of atmospheric electricity to
which appeal has been made from the earliest years of investigations of the UFO phenomena is that of ball lightning. For
example, a fairly extensive discussion of ball lightning was prepared by the U.S. Weather Bureau for inclusion in the 1949
(Air Force) Project Grudge report. It was concluded in that
report that ball lightning was most unlikely as an explanation for
any of the cases which were considered in that report (about
250). Periodically, in succeeding years, one or another writer has
come up with that same idea that maybe people who report
UFOs are really seeing ball lightning. No one ever tried to pursue
this idea very far, until P. J. Klass began writing on it. Although
his ideas have received some attention in magazines, there is
little enough scientific backup to his contentions that they are
quite unlikely to have the same measure of effect that Menzel's
previous writings have had. For that reason, I shall not here
elaborate on my strong objections to Klass's arguments. . . .
Klass has ignored most of what is known about ball lightning
and most of what is known about plasmas and also most of what
is known about interesting UFOs in developing his curious thesis.
It cannot be regarded as a scientifically significant contribution
to illumination of the UFO problem.

In his summary and recommendations, Dr. McDonald emphasizes that his personal study of the UFO problem has convinced him that "we must rapidly escalate serious scientific attention to this extraordinarily intriguing puzzle."
He goes on to say:

I believe that the scientific community has been seriously misinformed for twenty years about the potential importance of UFOs. . . . The possibility that the Earth might be under surveillance by some high civilization in command of a technology far beyond ours must not be overlooked in weighing the UFO problem. I am one of those who lean strongly towards the extraterrestrial hypothesis. I arrived at that point by a process of elimination of other alternative hypotheses, not by arguments on what I could call "irrefutable proof." I am convinced that the recurrent observations by reliable citizens here and abroad over the past twenty years cannot be brushed aside as nonsense, but rather need to be taken extremely seriously as evidence that some phenomenon is going on which we simply do not understand.

Dr. McDonald's conclusions, drawn from direct personal investigation of scores of carefully screened cases, stand in direct opposition to those of Dr. Condon. It is true that, in the study of UFOs, different scientists can look at the same data and come up with different conclusions. But if the "one white crow" theory is accepted, the thrust of the Condon Report is not negative; it is positive. The astronaut sightings and many of the radar-visual sightings are enough to establish the fact that white crows are possible if not probable. Certainly, in turn, this should call for further vigorous research, not withdrawal.

# 3.

WITH Dr. McDonald's testimony completed, the House committee turned its attention next to the testimony of Dr. Carl Sagan:

Mr. Roush. Our next participant is Dr. Carl Sagan.

Dr. Sagan is associate professor of astronomy in the Department of Astronomy and Center for Radiophysics and Space Research in Cornell University, having just recently left Harvard University. He has written over 100 scientific papers, and several articles for Encyclopedia Britannica, Americana. He is coauthor of several books. Dr. Sagan, we are delighted you are participating with us in this symposium this morning and you may proceed.

Dr. Sagan. Thank you very much, Congressman Roush.

As I understand what the committee would like from me, is a discussion of the likelihood of intelligent extraterrestrial life, and since this estimate is to be made in this symposium, clearly it is the hypothesis that unidentified objects are of extraterrestrial origin which the committee must have in mind.

I'm delighted to tell about contemporary scientific thinking along these lines, but let me begin by saying that I do not think the evidence is at all persuasive, that UFO's are of intelligent extraterrestrial origin, nor do I think the evi-

dence is convincing that no UFO's are of intelligent extraterrestrial origin.

I think as each of the preceding speakers has mentioned,
but perhaps not sufficiently emphasized, that the question
is very much an open one, and it is certainly too soon to
harden attitudes and make any permanent contentions on
the subject.

I find that the discussion, like elsewhere, is best evaluated
if we consider the question of life on earth. I suppose that
if you had all your prejudices removed and were concerned
with the question of whether the earth was populated by
life of any sort, how would you go about finding out?

If, for example, we were on some other planet, let's say
Mars, and looking at the Earth, what would we see? Fortunately we now have meteorological satellite photographs
of the earth at various resolutions, so we can answer the
question. The first large slide.

This is a photograph of the earth. That is the full earth,
which you are looking at which is primarily cloud cover.
This is the Pacific Ocean. You can see southern California
in the upper right, and, as advertised by the local chamber
of commerce, you can see it is cloud free. [Laughter.]

Now, it is clear that very little information about the
earth, much less possibility of life on it, is obtained by a
picture at this resolution.

The next large slide is a TIROS photograph of the earth
at about 1-mile resolution, that is, things smaller than a mile
cannot be seen, and very prolonged scrutiny of the entire
eastern seaboard of the United States shows no sign of life,
intelligent, or otherwise.

We have looked at several thousand photographs of the
earth, and you may be interested to see that there is no sign
of life, not only in New York or Washington, but also in
Peking, Moscow, London, Paris, and so on.

The reason is that human beings have transformed the earth at this kind of scale very little, and therefore the artifacts of human intelligence are just not detectable photographically in the daytime with this sort of resolution.

The next slide shows one of the few successful finds of intelligent life on earth that we made: down toward the lower left you can see a kind of grid, a kind of crisscross pattern, a rectangular area. This is a photograph taken near Cochran, Ontario, in Canada. What we are looking at are swaths cut by loggers through the forest. They cut many swaths in parallel, then another parallel sequence of swaths at right angles. Then the snow fell, heightening contrast, so that is the reason for the tic-tac-toe pattern. The sequence of straight lines there is anomalous. You would not expect it by geological processes. If you found that on another planet you would begin to expect there is life there. This is a photograph at about a tenth of a mile resolution, and is far better than the best photographs we have of Mars. The photographs we have of Mars are, of course, better than of any other planet. Therefore, to exclude intelligent life on another planet photographically is certainly premature. We could not exclude life on earth with this same sort of resolution.

However, there are other reasons why intelligent life on the other planets of this solar system are moderately unlikely.

To continue this sequence of photographs, I should say there are only about one in a thousand photographs where this resolution of the earth gives any sign of life.

The next photograph, however, shows a resolution about three times better. That is a Gemini capsule in the lower left-hand corner and we are looking at the vicinity of the Imperial Valley in California. You are just on the verge of resolving the contour patterns of fields, for agricultural purposes.

The next slide shows us an area between Sacramento and San Francisco, which has a very clear geometric pattern. It is quite obvious that this is the result of some intelligent activity on the earth.

You can see an airport, a railway, the monotonous pattern of housing developments in the upper right. You can see the patterns of contour fields. And this is such a highly geometrized picture, that it is clearly the result of some intelligence.

However, a photograph taken of this same area, only let's say 100,000 years ago, when there certainly was lots of life on earth, would show none of these features, because these are all the signs of our present technical civilization.

So even though the earth was full of life, and human beings were very much in evidence 100,000 years ago, none of this would be detectable by such photography. To detect individual organisms on earth, we have to have a photographic resolution about 10 times better than this, then we occasionally see things like these in the next slide. All those little dots casting shadows are cows in a field in California.

There are other ways of detecting intelligent life on the earth. From the vantage point of Mars, detecting, say, the lights of cities at night, is extremely marginal, and in fact the only way of doing it would be to point a small radio telescope at the earth, and then as the North American Continent turned toward Mars, there would be this blast of radio emission from domestic television transmission that prolonged scrutiny would indicate some sign of intelligent life on the earth.

In fact, it is radio communications which is the only reasonable method of communications over very large distances. It is a remarkable fact that the largest radio telescope on the earth at the present time, the Arecibo dish in Puerto Rico, is capable of communicating with another dish, similarly outfitted if one existed at the incredible distance of

1,000 light years away, a light year being about 6.6 trillion miles, and the distance to the nearest star being a little over 4 light years.

Now, let me then go to the question of the cosmic perspective of where we are.

We are, of course, sitting on a planet, the third from the Sun, which is going around the Sun, which is a star-like, and the other stars visible on a clear night to the naked eye.

The first small slide will give an impression of what happens when you point a moderate telescope in the direction of the center of the Milky Way Galaxy.

This is a photograph of a star cloud. You are looking at tens of thousands of suns here. In fact, the number of suns in our galaxy is about 150,000 million.

They are collected into a disc-shaped pattern, shown in the next slide; the next slide will show a photograph of the nearest galaxy like our own. That fuzzy spiral thing in the middle is M-31, that is also known as the Great Galaxy Andromeda, and if that were a photograph of our galaxy, we would be situated extremely far out, in fact, a little far off the slide, very much in the galactic boon docks. The Sun is nowhere near the center of the galaxy. It is a very out-of-the-way rural location we happen to be in.

Now, in collection of 150,000 million stars in the Milky Way Galaxy, our sun is just one, and there are at least billions of other galaxies, and the last slide will show you what happens if you point a telescope away from the obscuring dust and stars in the galaxy. You then start seeing dozens of other galaxies, everyone of those funny-shaped spiral and irregular-shaped things there, and some of the spherical-shaped ones, are other galaxies, each of which are containing about 100 billion stars as well.

So it is clear that there are in the accessible universe, some hundreds of billions of billions of stars, all more or less like our own.

Now, if we want to assess the likelihood that there are intelligent civilizations somewhere in advance of our own, on planets of other stars in our own galaxy, we have to ask questions which cover a variety of scientific subjects, some of which are fairly well known, some of which are extremely poorly known. For a numerical assessment of whether there is likely intelligence in other parts of the galaxy in a form we do not have at present, let me indicate the kinds of things we know. It depends on the rate of star formation.

It depends on the likelihood that the given star has planets. It depends on the likelihood at least one of those planets is at a position from the essential star which is suitable for the origin of life. It depends on the likelihood that the origin of life actually occurs on that planet. It depends on the probability life once arisen on that planet will evolve to some intelligence. It depends on the likelihood that intelligence, once emerged, will develop a technical civilization. And it depends on the lifetime of the technical civilization, because technical civilization of a very short lifetime will result in very few technical civilizations being around at any given time. We know something about some of these. There is some reason to believe that planets are a reasonable likely accompaniment of star formation, that the solar system in other words is a fairly common event in the galaxy and is not unique. There are laboratory experiments on the origin of life, in which the early conditions on earth have been duplicated in the laboratory. It turns out that at least the molecules fundamental to living systems, are produced relatively easy [sic], physics and chemistry apparently made in such a way that the origin of life may be a likely event.

Beyond that it is difficult to do laboratory experiments, because evolution takes billions of years, and scientists aren't that patient. Therefore, it is just a question of intelligent and knowledgeable estimates.

Here, some scientists believe that the evolution of intelligence and technical civilization is very likely. Others believe it is a very remarkable and unusual event and by the merest fluke did it happen here.

I don't think that this is the place to go into this very difficult question in any great detail. Let me merely say that much more important than these uncertainties is the question of the life of a technical civilization, judging from the events on the earth, one might say the likelihood of our civilization lasting only a few decades more, might be a fairly high probability, and if that is typical of other civilizations, then it is clear there aren't any other humans around.

On the other hand, if civilizations tend to have very long lifetimes, it may be there are large numbers of technical civilizations in the galaxy.

Now, one thing is clear, which is this: If there are other technical civilizations, any random one of them is likely to be vastly in advance of our own technical civilization. For example, we are only 10 or 15 years into having the technology of interstellar communication by radio astronomy. It is unlikely there is any other civilization in the galaxy that is that backward in their technical expertise.

Mr. MILLER. Doctor, didn't Sir Bernard Lovell receive electrical pulses he can't explain?

Dr. SAGAN. Yes, sir. There are now five objects in the heavens called pulsars, which are objects which are sending out radiation which is modulated with a frequency of about one per second; also there are submodulations. There are a variety of hypotheses to explain these things, some of which involve the oscillations of very old stars. There are certain difficulties with each hypothesis. The first suggestion made by the British at Cambridge, when they encountered this phenomenon was perhaps it was a beacon of some extraterrestrial civilization. That is not now their favored hypothesis. It is not clear that that is totally absurd, but in fact the scientific method to be used in that case is rather similar to the one to be used in this case. That is, it is a puzzling phenomenon. One therefore excludes all physical explanations that one possibly can before going to the much more hypothetical possibility of intelligence being involved.

So, that is the present state of work in that field. For data gathering to get better information, and the refinement of the purely physical hypothesis.

Well, I was saying that if there are other civilizations, many of them are likely to be far in advance of our own, and this, therefore, raises the question of how likely it is that they can traverse interstellar space and come from planets or some other star to here.

I should first emphasize that the distances between the stars are absolutely huge. Light, faster than which nothing can travel, takes 4½ years to get from here to the nearest star.

Mr. ROUSH. Excuse me, isn't that a rather arbitrary statement?

Dr. SAGAN. I don't think so. Perhaps you can tell me why you think it might be, then I can tell you why I think it isn't.

Mr. ROUSH. In my opening statement I referred to the new audacity of imagination John Dewey had spoken of. I'm thinking of imaginative terms, not factual terms.

Dr. SAGAN. Let me say in a sentence, why most physicists believe no material object can travel faster than light. That takes us into questions of the theory of relativity, which has had previous encounters with congressional committees, and perhaps we don't want to go into that in very great detail.

But the essential point is, that in making a few, very few assumptions, one of which was, the one we are talking about, nothing goes faster, Einstein was able to then derive a whole body of predictions which are confirmed in vast detail. Therefore, if someone says that is not a good idea, that things can travel faster than light, then they have to come up with a physical theory which explains everything we know in a way that is consistent with the idea that you can travel faster than light. No one has succeeded in doing that. Many physicists have tried. Therefore, the present belief is that you can't. But that, of course, is a time-dependent statement. It may be that this isn't the ultimate truth.

In physics, as in much of all science, there are no permanent truths. There is a set of approximations, getting closer and closer, and people must always be ready to revise what has been in the past thought to be the absolute gospel truth. If I might say, to revise opinions, is one which is frequent in science, and less frequent in politics. [Laughter.]

So, in the context of contemporary science, I'm obviously speaking in that context, one cannot travel faster than light.

So the distances between the stars are extremely large. Of course, any contemporary space vehicle would take a ridiculous amount of time to get from here to anywhere else, but we are not talking about contemporary space vehicles. The question, "Is there any conceivable method of traveling from one place to another very close to the speed of light, and therefore get reasonable transit times?" involves extrapolations of technology of a very difficult sort. However, let me merely say at least some people who have looked into the subject have concluded that it is not out of the question, even with contemporary principles of science, to imagine vehicles capable of traveling close to the speed of light, between the stars.

This doesn't mean that it happens. There may in fact be insuperable engineering difficulties we don't know about, but there is nothing in the physics that prohibits interstellar space flight.

So any estimate of how likely it is that we would be visited by an extraterrestrial intelligent civilization, depends not only on how many of them are there, but on what kind of transport they have, and how often they launch their space vehicles, even very optimistic estimates for all these numbers, gives a conclusion that an advance civilization comes here very rarely. But I again emphasize the great uncertainty in any of these numerical estimates, as they involve parts of science we don't know very much about.

So, to conclude what I understand is the main reason why this committee has asked me to testify, it is not beyond any question of doubt that we can be visited. There are great difficulties from our present point of view. They are not insuperable. And if Dr. McDonald, for example, were to present me with extremely convincing evidence of an advanced technology in a UFO, I could not say to him that is impossible, because I know you can't get from there to here, or I can't say to him that is impossible because I know there aren't any other guys up there.

On the other hand, I would of course demand very firm evidence before I would say, well, that seems to be a very likely hypothesis.

So I would like to spend just a few minutes to come more closely to the subject of this symposium.

First of all, I think it is clear to the committee, but this point should be emphasized very strongly, that there are very intense, predisposing, emotional factors in this subject.

There are individuals who very strongly want to believe that UFO's are of intelligent extraterrestrial origin. Essentially to my view, for religious motives; that is, things are so bad down here, maybe somebody from up there will come and save us from ourselves. This takes all sorts of subtle and not so subtle forms. There are also predisposing emotional factors in the other direction; people who very much want to believe UFO's are not of intelligent extraterrestrial origins, because that would be threatening to our conception of us as being the pinnacle of creation. We would find it very upsetting to discover that we are not, that we are just a sort of two-bit civilization.

It is clear that the scientific method says you don't take either of those views, and you simply keep an open mind and pursue whatever facts are at hand with as many diverse hypotheses as possible, and try to eliminate each suggested hypothesis, and see if you are lucky with any one.

I might mention that, on this symposium, there are no individuals who strongly disbelieve in the extraterrestrial origin of UFO's and therefore there is a certain view, not necessarily one I strongly agree with—but there is a certain view this committee is not hearing today, along those lines.

Finally, let me say something about the question of priorities, which Congressman Rumsfeld asked us for, and the question of significance.

Now, the possibility of discovering something about extraterrestrial life, life originated on some other planet, is of the very highest interest for biology and in fact for all science. A bona fide example of extraterrestrial life even in a very simple form, would revolutionize biology. It would have both practical and fundamental scientific benefits, which are very hard to assess, it would truly be immense.

Now, if the answer to this sort of profound scientific question lies right at hand, it would be folly to ignore it. If we are being visited by representatives of extraterrestrial life, just stick our heads in the sand, would be a very bad policy, I think.

On the other hand, to mount a major effort to investigate these things, I think requires some harder evidence than is now at hand.

It is clear that if such an effort were mounted, some information on atmospheric physics would be forthcoming. I think some information on psychology would certainly be forthcoming. I have the impression that the capability of human populations to self-delusion, has not been accorded appropriate weight in these considerations. There is an interesting book published about a century ago by McKay called "Extraordinary Popular Delusions and the Madness of Crowds," which I commend to the committee. It goes into such things as alchemy, and witchcraft. After all, there have been centuries in which these things were considered to be as obviously true as anything, and yet we now know that this is really nonsense.

So the possibility of these sort of delusions having a kind of contemporary guise as UFO's should not be thrown out altogether. I do not think that explains most or all of the unidentified settings.

Since the funds are so painfully tragically short for science today, the priority question boils down to this: In the search for extraterrestrial life there is a high risk, high possibility, that is the one we are talking about today; namely, UFO's— there is a high risk that they are not of extraterrestrial origin, but if they are, we are sure going to learn a lot.

Compared to that, there is a moderate risk, significant return possibility, and that is, looking for life even simple forms on nearby planets, and searching for intelligent radio communications by the techniques of radio astronomy. Here it is clear there would be significant paydirt of one sort or another for what I gather is a comparable sort of investment.

So if Congress is interested, and I'm not sure it is, I think it might very well ought to be, but if Congress is interested in a pursuit of the question of extraterrestrial life, I believe it would be much better advised to support the biology, the Mariner, and Voyager programs of NASA, and the radio astronomy programs of the National Science Foundation, than to pour very much money into this study of UFO's.

On the other hand, I think a moderate support of investigations of UFO's might very well have some scientific paydirt in it, but perhaps not the one that we are talking about today.

Mr. Chairman, that concludes my statement except that I request that you include for the record a statement entitled "Unidentified Flying Objects" that I prepared for the Encyclopedia Americana.

Thank you.

Mr. HECHLER. Dr. Sagan, there have been some recent experiments at Green Bank, W. Va., with its 300-foot telescope, in an attempt to synchronize this with the Arecibo dish, in such a way as you might in effect produce almost a 2,000-mile diameter collecting surface for trying to receive signals from the pulsars.

I wonder if this isn't the type of specific activity in radio astronomy that could utilize some additional support in order to ascertain the truth about terrestrial life and signals therefrom?

Dr. SAGAN. Congressman Hechler, as a member of the faculty at Cornell that runs the observatory, I would find some problem answering that.

Mr. HECHLER. But not of West Virginia, however?

Dr. SAGAN. That is right. The study of pulsars, as I indicated to Chairman Miller, is relevant. The development of a long base-line parameter of the sort you talked about is of great interest to many areas of radio astronomy, and conceivably to the area we are talking about.

However, there has not been since Project OXMA, which occurred in Green Bank some 7 years or so ago, any systematic effort in this country to look for signals of intelligent extraterrestrial origin.

There is at the present time a fairly major effort under way in the Soviet Union, but at least in this country there are no such efforts directed specifically to this question.

It may be if we ever do detect intelligent signals from elsewhere, it will be an accidental byproduct of some other program. There is at the present time no effort to search for extraterrestrial signals.

Chairman MILLER. Are they trying to do things in Australia?

Dr. SAGAN. To the best of my knowledge there is no such work being done.

Chairman MILLER. The Mills-Cross program is also connected with Cornell, isn't it?

Dr. SAGAN. The Cornell-Sydney Astronomy Center, yes, sir.

Chairman MILLER. Is that all, Mr. Hechler?

Mr. HECHLER. I was hoping you would suggest something more specific, for our future consideration.

Dr. SAGAN. Let me say, and again let me emphasize that it is by no means demonstrated that radio astronomical searches for extraterrestrial intelligence have anything whatever to do with UFO's, but if we were interested, as some of us are, in examining the possibility of extraterrestrial intelligence, sending signals to Earth, then relatively modest programs, of say less than a million dollars, could be organized, using largely existing instruments with only small modifications in the things you hook up to the radio telescope, which would be ideal for this purpose.

There are in fact many radio astronomers who are privately interested in this sort of thing, but it carries something of the same sort of stigma that both the previous speakers mentioned about UFO's. It is unconventional. It is in many senses radical. Many astronomers prefer to have nothing to do with it.

Mr. PETTIS. Mr. Chairman.

Mr. ROUSH. Mr. Pettis.

Mr. PETTIS. I would like to ask the doctor, or any other member of the panel. Is there any indication that any other Government, particularly the Russians, are interested in this subject?

Dr. SAGAN. I cannot speak about the UFO program. Perhaps Dr. Hynek can say something about that.

As far as the question that I just mentioned, the radio search for extraterrestrial intelligence, there is a state commission in the Soviet Union, for the investigation of cosmic-radio intelligence. There is a fairly major effort that has been mustered for the last few years along these lines.

And there is only some information about that; that we have gotten out of the Soviet Union.

I don't know anything about their activities on UFO's. Perhaps Dr. Hynek would like to comment on that.

Dr. HYNEK. May I, Mr. Chairman, preface my remark, in answer to that, by pointing out a danger here that we may be putting the cart before the horse in the consideration of extraterrestrial intelligence.

Speaking of horses, suppose someone comes here and tells us, or announces to us there is a report of a horse in the bath tub.

I think that it would be rather pointless to then ask, what is the color of the horse, what does he eat, how could he have gotten there, who installed the bath tub? The question is is there is a horse in the bath tub? This is a question I think we should direct ourselves to first. Is there anything to these reports?

Now, coming to the question of the Russian situation, I do know from my visits behind the Iron Curtain, or as they like to speak of it, the Socialist countries, there have been sightings behind the Iron Curtain.

In fact, if you were to have good translations, it would be difficult to distinguish between a UFO report from Russia, from Brazil, from Argentina, from Japan, or from the United States. There is a rather rough pattern.

Now, the Russians, to the best of my knowledge, have given no official recognition to the problem, but I do know, from personal information, that there is sort of a ground-swell interest, or a latent interest, that pops up here and there, but apparently they have as much difficulty in getting official recognition as we do.

Mr. ROUSH. I would first point out that I realize that a visit to Russia doesn't necessarily make a person an expert or give him all the information. A year ago June I did visit Russia. I had conversations with a few of their people, including, my pronunciation may not be correct, Dr. Millionshchikov and the head of their weather bureau, I believe it is Petrov, and several others, and I repeatedly asked the question, "Do you believe in unidentified flying objects?" In each instance they merely laughed. That was the response that I got. Since then, however, I have observed there have been papers published in Russia discussing the phenomena, and discussing it in scientific terms.

It seems to me that any discussion such as ours today raises the question of the existence of extraterrestrial life. That is one reason we asked Dr. Sagan to come here. I'm not real sure, Dr. Sagan, whether you stated whether there is or whether there is not extraterrestrial life. I was watching for that, and I don't believe I heard you say it.

Dr. SAGAN. Congressman Roush, I have enough difficulty trying to determine if there is intelligent life on Earth, to be sure if there is intelligent life anywhere else. [Laughter.]

If we knew there was life on other planets, then we would be able to save ourselves a lot of agony finding out. It is just because the problem is so significant, and we don't have the answers at hand we need to pursue the subject. I don't know. It beats me.

Mr. ROUSH. I believe you coauthored a book with a Russian, is that correct?

Dr. SAGAN. That is correct.

Mr. ROUSH. Does Dr. Shklovskii share your views?

Dr. SAGAN. I think he shares my restraint.

I think both of us would say we think this is an extremely important subject, that we are on the frontier of being able to find out, but that neither of us knows whether there is or isn't life out there. Let me say if it turns out there isn't life on Mars, that is almost as interesting as if we find there is life on Mars, because then we have to ask, what happened different on Mars than on the Earth, so that life arose here and not there. That will surely give us a very profound entry into the question of follow-up of evolution and the cosmic context.

Mr. ROUSH. Suppose we discover there is life on Mars, in some form, wouldn't this almost cinch your case, and you could say there is extraterrestrial life?

Dr. SAGAN. Yes, sir; it certainly would, but not cinch our case about extraterrestrial intelligence. Conceivably, there might be a low form on Mars. If there is Martian life, it is of interest how low it is. If there is intelligence on Mars—but we don't know there is intelligence on Mars—then we don't have to grasp that evolution process.

Mr. ROUSH. I would like to finish this morning's session just by telling of a cartoon I saw which I think Dr. Hynek perhaps saw and enjoyed as much as I did. It showed a flying saucer hovering over the Earth, with little green men looking down, and one turned to the other and said, "Do you suppose it is swamp gas?" [Laughter.]

Dr. HYNEK. That is a good statement to close the session on.

Mr. ROUSH. We shall reconvene at 2 o'clock this afternoon.

Dr. Sagan's stance about UFOs seemed to rest somewhere in between the restrained advocacy of Dr. Hynek and Dr. McDonald and the blatant negativism of Dr. Condon, filling in a needed spot in the spectrum of opinion. His outlook would have probably been ideal for the Colorado-Air Force study because of its cool objectivity. He had not, however, been exposed to the intensive personal investigations experienced by both Dr. Hynek and Dr. McDonald, and the question remains whether he, as they did, might have become almost reluctantly convinced of the urgency of most intensive further study if he had appraised the accumulated evidence directly.

In his article for the *Encyclopedia Americana,* which he read into the record, he seems to put too much credence in the Air Force statistics. Careful scrutiny of these has definitely established them as not only inconsistent but grossly inaccurate. But his approach is open and detached, and a welcome contrast to that displayed by Dr. Condon.

He admits that although interstellar space flight is far beyond our present technical capabilities, there is no fundamental physical objection to it. He also concludes that it would be rash to preclude the possibility of interstellar travel capabilities by other civilizations.

In the light of his objectivity, it is noteworthy that he feels that the UFO question is very much an open one, and attitudes should not be hardened at this time as Dr. Condon has suggested in his conclusions. While Sagan does not think that the evidence of UFOs being extraterrestrial is at all persuasive, he is equally persuaded that the evidence *against* this hypothesis is not convincing.

His comment about the Tiros photograph, in which things on the earth smaller than one mile cannot be seen, is most interesting and informative. In other words, looking at the earth from this vantage point, the entire Eastern seaboard appears to be totally without life or civilization.

His short lecture on cosmic perspective is also compelling enough to shatter our homocentric provincialism. With hundreds of billions of suns similar to ours, most astronomers and scientists agree with Dr. Sagan today that the evolution of intelligence and technical civilization on some of their planets is most likely. This, coupled with the agreement of some scientists that there is nothing in physics that prohibits interstellar flight, makes the UFO case at least within the realm of possibility.

This is a very important point. Without this possible concept being realistically granted, the idea of UFOs as extraterrestrial vehicles should most certainly be relegated to the trash heap.

The sightings behind the Iron Curtain brought up in the discussion that followed Dr. Sagan's presentation are important, because they indicate some puzzlement in that camp and suggest that others may be as perplexed as we are about the subject. The negative conclusions of Dr. Condon will have an extremely deleterious effect on any worldwide studies, since many intelligent persons throughout Europe and Asia with whom I spoke indicated that they looked to the United States for ultimate opinion on UFOs. It is interesting that in the Colorado report Dr. Condon should have chosen Dr. Menzel to assemble the worldwide data, probably one of the most negatively prejudiced individuals he could have appointed. Menzel's findings for the foreign scene are in sharp contrast to the attitude I found personally around the world; and if his investigations in these areas for the Condon Report are so shallow as the manner in which he investigated the Exeter case, his conclusions can only be considered as useless. Yet again they are clothed in an aura of pseudo-authority that is simply not merited. The close-range sightings are the most important, because the hundreds of these cases involve UFOs at either ground level or up to a hundred feet or so. An astronomer has no more expertise in these altitudes than does an intelligent layman. Dr. Menzel seems to think otherwise.

With the conclusion of Dr. Sagan's testimony, the hearings adjourned for lunch. In the afternoon, further testimony from other scientists would be offered which would certainly be of a nature to throw further doubt on the Condon-Menzel school of thought.

# 4.

THE theory of mass hysteria as the principal source of UFO reports has often been invoked, and frequently by those who are non-expert in the subject. That is why the first scientist to testify after the luncheon break created considerable interest in his psychological assessment of UFO sightings.

Mr. ROUSH. The committee will be in order.

This afternoon we are going to hear first from Dr. Robert L. Hall. Dr. Hall is professor and head of the Department of Sociology at the University of Illinois, and has been since 1965.

He too has a distinguished career. Dr. Hall, we are glad to welcome you as a participant in this symposium, and you may proceed.

Dr. HALL. Thank you, Mr. Roush.

First I should like to state a few of the rather well-established facts as they would be seen by a social psychologist. I find that when I do so, there is a great deal of redundancy. You have heard most of these facts before, so I will make my presentation brief.

Fundamentally what we know that everyone can agree upon is that a great many people all over the world keep reporting some quite puzzling flying objects. In these reports there are certain recurring features, and the people so reporting often have all the characteristics of reliable witnesses.

Second, the next main thing we know is that there are several strongly, often bitterly competing systems of belief about how to explain these observations, and some rational men seem to fall into line supporting each of these positions.

This in itself is of course of great interest to a social psychologist. Inevitably he is interested in how systems of belief grow and are maintained.

The third major factual thing that can be quite well agreed upon is that to a very large extent these alternative explanations, these systems of belief, have become rooted in organizations of people who have become committed to defending their respective positions. This greatly complicates the problem of arriving at a generally accepted explanation. In that sense, in addition to any other problems that have been defined here, clearly we have a social psychological problem also.

These are very briefly the main outlines of the facts as I see them. Now, how are these explained?

There are certain things that everyone seems to agree upon, or nearly everyone, I believe. First that a great many of these observations can be quite clearly identified as mistakes on the part of the observer, misidentifications of familiar objects, hoaxes, and a miscellaneous collection of similar things.

Beyond that point, there comes to be a good deal of divergence in explanations, to say the least. Perhaps the major views now can be classified simply as follows: First, that these are technological devices or vehicles of some sort entering our atmosphere from the outside.

Second, that this is some new, as yet ill-understood natural phenomena [sic], something like a form of plasma, that we do not understand, and so on.

The third major hypothesis to explain the hard-core cases

that are not otherwise agreed upon, is that they too are simply a result of mass hysteria, and its resulting misidentifications.

This hypothesis I will address myself to particularly very soon, because obviously a social psychologist has a special interest in this possibility.

The three major topics that I believe I should address myself to are, first, what has brought about this complicated situation of strongly opposed beliefs that seem to resist the factual evidence, and are not responsive to each other?

Second, what are the probable consequences from the point of view of a sociologist or social psychologist of each of the major explanations?

And third, I would like to comment quite explicitly on the hypothesis that mass hysteria and hysterical contagion is common in many of the cases.

I believe I should start with the mass hysteria hypothesis. To begin with, I think there is very strong evidence that some of the cases do result from hysterical contagion in the sense that this has often been used by social psychologists. Once people are sensitized to the existence of some kind of a phenomenon (whether indeed it really exists or not), when there is an ambiguous situation requiring explanation, when there is emotion or anxiety associated with this, resulting from the uncertainty, there are precisely the conditions that have been observed repeatedly as resulting in what I shall call "improvised news." Lacking well-verified facts and explanations, people always seem to generate the news and the explanations that will reduce the ambiguity, thereby reduce the anxiety they have about uncertain situations.

There are many well-documented cases of this kind of mass hysteria and hysterical contagion. I believe it will be out of place for me to go into lengthy discussions of these episodes, but I shall comment on a few ways in which we can examine the observations of unidentified flying objects to assess whether this is a reasonable hypothesis for the hard-core cases.

One of the first of these is one thoroughly familiar to attorneys, social psychologists having no monopoly on an interest in the credibility of testimony, but this is one of the principal means obviously of establishing whether we should reasonably believe explanations.

The criteria, as most of you know, involve such things as the established reputation of the witnesses, the quality and details of the report, whether there are apparent motives for distortion or prevarication, whether there was preexisting knowledge of the thing being reported, whether there were multiple witnesses and whether there was contact among these multiple witnesses, whether observation was through more than one medium (for example, direct visual observation confirmed by radar) whether there were verifiable effects that could be observed after the reporting by witnesses, recently of the events being reported, the duration of the period in which the witness was able to observe the phenomenon; how the witnesses reacted, whether they had intense anxiety and emotion themselves, which might interfere with their observation, and so forth.

These are some of the major factors, and a closely related factor in assessing the credibility of the testimony is of course an assessment of the care in gathering the testimony by interviewers themselves.

How does the testimony on hard-core UFO cases look with reference to these criteria? I should say that there is a substantial subset of cases which look very good on these criteria, which make it very difficult to say that the witnesses involved were victims of hysterical contagion, grossly misinterpreting familiar things.

For example, there is the Red Bluff, Calif., case in 1960, where two policemen observed for 2 hours and 15 minutes constantly, apparently without tremendous anxiety or concern, an object hovering, moving about, going through gyrations. Twice it approached their police car. When they tried to approach it, it would retreat.

They radioed in and requested that this object be confirmed on radar, and it was confirmed by local radar stations at approximately the same location.

Ultimately, after a couple of hours of observation, they watched this object move away, join a second similar object, and then disappear. They then went to the sheriff's office, where two deputies were present who had also seen this phenomenon, and gave similar descriptions.

Now applying the criteria to a case such as this, in most respects it is very convincing. These are police officers of good reputation. Their report was prompt, thorough, careful, and in writing—and I have read the report in full. There is much detail in it of a sort that could be cross-checked with the other witnesses from the sheriff's office. There are no apparent motives for prevarication or distortion. It was a long period of observation.

I cannot establish very clearly what prior interest or information these witnesses had, but I find no indication that they had any. There was confirmation of the observation from more than one medium of observation—both visual and radar.

This is the kind of case that leads me to regard the hypothesis of hysterical contagion as being quite inadequate to account for these observations. It is not a lone case; there are many others.

There were trained ground observers near White Plains, N.Y., in 1954, who observed an object which they described as having the apparent size of the moon, while simultaneously they saw the moon, which was not full that night. They watched this for 20 or 30 minutes, then it moved away to the southeast.

Two radar stations established fixes confirming the visually reported location. Jets were scrambled from two bases to intercept. The ground observers were able to see the jet trails approaching. Both the pilots of the jets and the ground observers report that as the jets approached, this object changed color and moved up very rapidly and disappeared, and at that point radar contact was also lost.

Once again this is the kind of report that seems to me to fit the customary criteria of credibility to a very considerable degree. It is very difficult to claim that these multiple observers, trained for the type of observation they were making, confirmed independently through more than one channel, were victims of hysterical contagion.

Dr. McDonald, I believe, referred briefly to the Levelland, Tex. cases in 1958, of interference with automobile ignition, in which there were 10 separate sightings in that one evening, apparently with no opportunity for the citizens involved either to read the news, hear the news of this, nor to talk with one another. They uniformly reported the same general shape. They uniformly reported—a great many of them reported also interference with automobiles ignition and headlights. This was an effect which at that time had not been observed and publicized a great deal. It subsequently has become publicized.

Now, how do these cases differ from the well-known, documented cases of mass hysteria and hysterical contagion? In general those episodes have not persisted as long as the active interest in unidentified flying objects. It lasted a week or a few weeks, and it had not been too difficult to find reasonably acceptable explanations.

In the second place, they have not generally involved a prolonged observation of a phenomenon by people who were calm, not emotionally upset. A characteristic example of hysterical contagion would be the recent study by Back and Kerckhoff, supported by the National Science Foundation. The book reporting on this study is called "The June Bug." It was a case of hysterical contagion among the employees of a factory in North Carolina.

It is one of the most thoroughly reported and studied incidents of this sort. It resembles the kind of thing we are talking about in almost no respect. I find it very difficult to find elements in common, other than the fact that some people believed something that was difficult to verify.

The employees were convinced that they were being bitten by poisonous insects, resulting in fainting and other symptoms such as rashes. All medical officers, all careful research on this, was unable to turn up any hard evidence that such an insect was present, or that there was any standard medical accounting for these symptoms. But these were people in close constant contact, sharing a particular set of problems and frustrations that raised their level of anxiety.

The epidemic can be interpreted as a convenient way of escaping the problem of coping with very difficult circumstances. I have said that I think in isolated cases you can find a similar thing in observations of unidentified flying objects, but if we look at the hard-core, well-documented cases, I see practically no resemblance.

Another important thing to note about the witnesses in the best sightings of UFO's is that very commonly—as has been mentioned, I believe, by Dr. McDonald—they first try to explain their observation in some very familiar terms. This is the well-known and labeled psychological process of "assimilation." People first try to assimilate their observation into something understood and known and familiar.

This is quite contrary to the kind of argument frequently built into the hypothesis of hysterical contagion, namely, that characteristically witnesses are eager, are motivated, to see strange objects.

Another important thing to notice about the witnesses in

these cases is of course their reluctance to report. We have had some mention of that. This, for one thing, counters the argument of publicity seeking as a motive in some of the best cases. It incidentally runs contrary to most experience of social psychologists engaged in public opinion research, in polling, and contrary to the experience of experienced precinct workers in politics. Those people who have not tried this kind of thing expect people not to want to talk to them, but when you start ringing doorbells, the striking thing about the American people is it is often difficult to stop them from telling you what they believe. Yet in instances of unidentified flying objects, there has often been a marked reluctance to talk about them.

I can illustrate this anecdotally simply to make my point. When I was on the faculty at the University of Minnesota, a student came to me, having heard that I had some interest in this question. He informed me that his father, a colonel, an artillery colonel in Korea—this was at the time of the Korean conflict—had flown over a hill in Korea in his observer plane, and found (right next to him virtually) a characteristic unidentified flying object with the usual kind of configuration. It had promptly retreated upwards. It had frightened him, but he was an experienced and trained observer, so he took notes on it; he recorded it. When he returned he was so ridiculed and laughed at for a long period of time that he completely gave up trying to have this taken seriously. He refused to talk about it.

I urged this student to get his father to report this to some of the private organizations that might take it seriously, and he apparently was unable to do so. The ridicule suppressed the opportunity for this information.

I have encountered similar things in academic colleagues from a variety of fields, finding they are very interested and wanting to hear about this, but are afraid to talk about.

In order to support the hysterical contagion hypothesis, it

seems to me we need to present some plausible evidence:

First, that there is a very ambiguous situation. This we can all agree upon.

Second, that there is a great deal of anxiety and concern about it. This appears clearly to be the case.

Third, some plausible evidence of contact among the witnesses, either directly by conversing with one another, or indirectly by being exposed to the same information, the same stimuli. In cases that I have studied, I find that this third element is the one that is often lacking, that there are often witnesses who appear not to have had prior knowledge, not to have had contact with one another, not to have been exposed, as far as we can determine, to the same news information.

I might throw in here, in reference to a remark Dr. Hynek made, that the public is indeed very unwilling to accept the kinds of casual and bland explanations that have been offered. This has been my experience also, and is indeed an index of the amount of concern and anxiety about this, it appears to me.

Now I will turn to another subject. I might summarize in one sentence that in my eyes the hypothesis that the hardcore cases of observed UFO's is hysterical contagion is highly improbable. The weight of evidence is strongly against it.

Now I would like to address the question of what has brought about this situation of strongly opposing beliefs that seem not to become reconciled with one another. On this I will have to digress first to explain briefly what I mean by a system of beliefs in social psychology.

Perhaps the best way to explain that is to say that just as nature abhors a vacuum, nature abhors an isolated belief. Neither a belief nor the person who holds it can normally persist very long in isolation. The beliefs become organized in such a way that, for one person, his various beliefs support one another, and people gather together in organizations to lend each other support in their beliefs. This is the sense in which we have highly developed systems of belief which come to resist change, to resist evidence.

The circumstances under which systems of belief such as this characteristically arise are, as I mentioned in passing before, a situation of ambiguity about a matter of importance on which there is not reliable, verified information in which people have confidence. Clearly the antidote is simple. It is to get good, reliable information which people have confidence in.

This is probably the only way to weaken the irrational elements that are strongly resistant.

Finally, I want to comment to some extent on the probable consequences of each of the most important explanations that has been offered, and what might be done in the public interest in each instance to counter the negative aspect of these consequences.

Let's suppose to start with that these are extraterrestrial devices of some sort visiting our atmosphere. If this is the case, we for one thing have to concern ourselves with the possible consequences of contact with civilizations which are technologically very advanced and whose values we know nothing about. It is very tempting to the anthropomorphic, to attribute human characteristics to any such life form hypothesized, and to imagine, like humans, they might be hostile and might cause us some danger.

I know of no hard evidence of danger, or threat, from the cases reported. But we do not have any inkling, if indeed these are extraterrestrial devices, as to their purpose. We have no hard evidence as to their purpose, their intent, their motives, so to speak.

Consequently, I find it extremely difficult to even speculate in an intelligent way about what might result from contact with them. I can say a very great risk of contact, if this is the case, is the risk of panic, and panic is often very harmful to us mere humans, as in theater fires and so on.

Once again from all knowledge in sociology and social psychology, the best way to counter this risk of panic is not to issue reassuring statements, but to find sound information in which people have confidence which can reduce their anxiety about the situation, and explain it adequately. This to me has been one of the most unfortunate and possibly dangerous aspects of this problem, that the ridicule, the tendency not to take the problem seriously, to issue reassurances rather than good information, has in my opinion only maximized the risk of panic, at least under this hypothesis, and I believe under the others as well.

Another risk, if these are extraterrestrial devices is clearly the risk of misinterpreting the devices as hostile devices from another country on earth, which might trigger indeed a devastating nuclear war. Once again, the same conclusions follow about the need for good information.

Mr. ROUSH. Might not another conclusion be that if there should be something to this, again, if there should be perhaps it would bring all the people of the world together for a better understanding, a common purpose, and a common stand, which probably would relieve us of some of our own anxieties?

Dr. HALL. This is indeed within the range of possibility, though I hesitate to speculate on the probability.

Mr. ROUSH. You don't have to speculate. Go ahead.

Dr. HALL. The final comment about probable effect, if these are indeed extraterrestrial devices, is of course the possibility of learning something of great technological value from them. The possible value of contact for purposes of advancing our knowledge of our technology.

Let's turn then to another hypothesis, which is this is a natural phenomenon which we do not understand, something like plasma. In this case, I think we have precisely the same risk of panic through misinterpretation resulting in precisely the same recommendation for the need for understanding to reduce the risk of panic.

I think we have precisely the same risk of misinterpretation as hostile aircraft, with again the same resulting recommendation.

I think we have again the same possible great value from understanding the phenomenon in order to advance our knowledge.

The third major hypothesis, explanation, which I cited above, is that even the most solid and plausible cases reported are results of mass hysteria and hysterical contagion. I simply note that if this is the case, I regard it as prima facie evidence that we badly need to improve our understanding of mass hysteria, of the process of belief formation, of the means by which we might control the kinds of anxiety that produce this problem.

In this situation there is still the dangerous risk of panic, even if there is no physical phenomenon underlying these reports. There is still the risk of misinterpretation of hostile aircraft, and I would submit that there is still the great potential benefit from studying it thoroughly and scientifically, in this case the gain being a gain in sociological and psychological knowledge, which would be of obvious importance if all of this is caused simply by mass hysteria.

I have a few conclusions and recommendations which I have written out. I will try to tie these to what others have said as I go along.

My first conclusion would be that no matter what explanation you accept, we have here a rare opportunity for gaining some useful knowledge by a thorough detached study of UFO reports, and a systematic gathering of new information, hopefully with good instrumentation, and good, well-trained interviewing teams.

My second conclusion would be that hysteria and contagion of belief can account for some of the reports, but there is strong evidence that there is some physical phenomena [*sic*] underlying a portion of the reports.

Third, I would conclude that because of the lack of trustworthy information the systems of conflicting beliefs has been built up to account for a very ambiguous set of circumstances. Each of these positions is sometimes defended beyond the point of rationality.

Fourth, I would repeat my earlier statement as a conclusion, that whether or not there is a physical phenomenon underlying a portion of the reports, we clearly have a social psychological problem of subduing these irrational systems of belief, defense of beliefs, of lowering the anxiety about these reports, and of reducing the ambiguity about their nature.

The recommendations that I had written out were two— excuse me, were three, and overlap considerably with the comments of my colleagues. I would say that the most important matter is to promote the fullest possible free circulation of all the available information about this phenomenon. This should help reduce risks of panic and other dangerous irrational actions. It should help to weaken these systems of belief, the irrational elements in them. Here I would say indifference, or disinterest on the part of national leaders can retard our learning about this phenomenon, and open interest and encouragement can help.

I believe you are performing a fine service in having this kind of open inquiry. This whole matter badly needs to be treated as something deserving serious study.

The second recommendation I have to make concerns some general lines of research that would seem to me called for. One of these seems to me would be to take the 100 or 200 cases per year that seem to be reliably reported and reasonably well documented, and to study them carefully for recurring patterns, with emphasis on the way they react to their environment, the way they react to light sources, the way they react to presence of humans and so on.

The second form of research would be, I think, to study explicitly those portions of the problem that do result from mass hysteria, apparently. These need to be studied intensively, quite apart from the question of the physical phenomena, to improve our understanding of mass hysteria and panic, and its possibly dangerous consequences.

In doing this I think it is terribly important that particular observations be studied by the scientists of a variety of disciplines, that the study of the hysteria hypothesis not be separated from the others. If it is, there is a tendency to make this hypothesis the garbage can for otherwise unexplained sightings.

The third type of study that seems to me terribly important, but my colleagues at the table can speak with more authority than I, is the systematic gathering of new cases with good scientific instrumentation, the kind of work in quantitative evidence that would give us much more to go on.

The third recommendation I had to suggest was that possibly in addition to a careful scientific investigation and study of this phenomenon, it might be fruitful to set up formally an adversary procceding modeled after our system of jurisprudence. There is a tendency for us academics to sit on fences as long as we possibly can, and I think that if there were several teams of investigators who were assigned the responsibility much the way a prosecuting attorney or defense attorney is, assigned the responsibility to make the strongest possible case for one of the systems of explanation, that this would challenge the others, and force them to find more solid evidence.

It would try to benefit from some of the valuable features we have in our system of jurisprudence.

That concludes my presentation, except to comment briefly on how this relates to the suggestion of my colleagues. I would certainly enthusiastically agree with Dr. Hynek's suggestion of a board of inquiry, or some competent group to study the phenomenon.

I would certainly agree with Dr. McDonald's view that a variety of approaches would be fruitful, that a single study has many disadvantages. I have taken an interest for a number of years in the problems of the support of academic institutions by Government, and I think that we are most likely to proceed to some good knowledge rapidly if we don't put all our eggs in one basket.

I certainly agree with Dr. Sagan's view that there are these very intense predisposing emotional factors for each of these beliefs. Somehow we need to weaken those.

Finally, on the idea of UN cooperation, this had not occurred to me, but I think it is an excellent idea. If it is possible to establish some detached international agency that can bring about free, open flow of information, and some cooperation internationally in investigating this, it would be helpful.

Thank you, Mr. Roush.

Mr. ROUSH. Thank you, Dr. Hall.

Dr. Hall's background, which includes studies in psychology and sociology at Yale, the University of Sweden, and the University of Minnesota, also includes psychological research on the performance of bomber crews and the role of the aircraft commander for the Air Force Personnel & Training Research Center. In conjunction with his appraisal of the UFOs, this is most valuable because it lends practical experience to the assessment of how aviation personnel react in extraordinary situations. Since many of the most interesting sightings arise from Air Force and commercial pilot sightings, Dr. Hall's observations carry the added weight of this experience. Further, the testimony comes from a man whose business it is to know the roots and extent of mass hysteria and its accompanying anomalies.

Dr. Hall subscribes to the theory that "credible people are seeing incredible things," and backs up the almost uncontested premise (even by Dr. Condon) that most of those who have viewed UFOs are sane and reliable witnesses. He also has turned attention to the fact that rational men tend to take strongly opposing sides in the controversy.

Dr. Hall does what Dr. Condon failed to do: he zeros in and concentrates exclusively on those hard-data cases that make up the real mystery. He grants that mass hysteria may account for some of the sightings, but indicates that this hypothesis simply does not apply to the hundreds of cases that are worth paying attention to. The case he cites of the two policemen who kept an object in sight for some two hours, time to summon and obtain radar confirmation, is alone enough to demand serious study instead of a brush-off.

Dr. Hall's appraisal of the *weight* of evidence is also in marked contrast to Dr. Condon's superficial view of this body of material. Hall points out that the typical reaction of a UFO witness is to try to explain a sighting first in ordinary terms, that the average witness, far from seeking publicity, tries to avoid it because of the ridicule factor.

His comments on the risk of panic if UFOs are determined to be extraterrestrial is most interesting. He argues that there is a possibility of panic, but that false reassurances would be far worse than the furnishing of straightforward information.

Dr. Hall's conclusions parallel those of nearly all the other scientists who testified on that day. He feels that much useful knowledge will emerge from the further continued study of the subject, that mass hysteria by no means explains the important cases, that both extremes of the controversy defend their points of view irrationally, and that there exists a major social problem regardless of whether or not the objects are extraterrestrial. He further agrees with Dr. Hynek's concept of a continuing board of study, tied into an international group of the same nature. But whatever the case, the free circulation of information is essential.

# 5.

DR. James A. Harder, who next took the stand, is associate professor of civil engineering at the University of California in Berkeley. He took his Ph.D. from Cal Tech, and has been a specialist in engineering science since that time. He has paid special attention to possible propulsion systems that might explain the unusual maneuvering of UFOs. He elaborates in further detail the police case brought up by Dr. Hall.

Dr. HARDER. Your committee has asked me to comment on the problem of propulsion as raised by some reports, and to whatever potential benefit there might be to the aerospace programs from an intense scrutiny of UFO phenomena.

I am very glad for this opportunity to present to your committee some of my views on the problems of unidentified flying objects and to indicate some of the areas in which I think a closer investigation of this problem might provide us with scientific clues that would give us important impetus to basic and applied research in the United States.

As Dr. Hall has said, there have been strong feelings aroused about UFO's, particularly about the extraterrestrial hypothesis for their origin. This is entirely understandable, in view of man's historic record of considering himself the central figure in the natural scene; the extraterrestrial hy-

pothesis tends inevitably to undermine the collective ego of
the human race. These feelings have no place in the scientific assessment of facts, but I confess that they have at
times affected me.

Over the past 20 years a vast amount of evidence has
been accumulating that bears on the existence of UFO's.
Most of this is little known to the general public or to most
scientists. But on the basis of the data and ordinary rules
of evidence, as would be applied in civil or criminal courts,
the physical reality of UFO's has been proved beyond a
reasonable doubt. With some effort, we can accept this on
an intellectual level but find a difficulty in accepting it on
an emotional level, in such a way that the facts give a feeling of reality. In this respect, we might recall the attitude
many of us have toward our own deaths: We accept the
facts intellectually, but find it difficult to accept them
emotionally.

Indeed, there are flying saucer cultists who are as enthusiastic as they are naïve about UFO's—who see in them
some messianic symbols—they have a counterpart in those
individuals who exhibit a morbid preoccupation with death.
Most of the rest of us don't like to think or hear about it.
This, it seems to me, accurately reflects many of our attitudes toward the reality of UFO's—natural, and somewhat
healthy, but not scientific.

In my remaining statements you will note that I have
tacitly assumed the reality of UFO's as a hypothesis underlying my assessment of the importance of this subject for
scientific study.

## 1. THE UFO PROPULSION PROBLEM

By way of introducing the propulsion problem of UFO's,
I will review a sighting near the city of Corning, in northern
California, during the night of August 13, 1960, by two

California highway patrolmen. During that night, and several succeeding nights, there were many reports of UFO's over northern California, but this particular event is important not only because of the fact that it has been well authenticated but because of the relatively long time and close nature of the observations. My condensed description that follows is from the official report filed the next day by the two officers (see appendix I and II) from a half-hour taped interview conducted 3 days later by myself and Dr. Carl Johannessen, of the University of Oregon; from a letter written by Officer Charles A. Carson to Walter N. Webb, Charles Hayden Planetarium, Boston, Mass., dated November 14, 1960; and from a telephoned interview conducted by Dr. James McDonald with Mr. Carson on October 27, 1966.

Officers Scott and Carson were searching for a speeding motorcyclist along Hoag Road, east of Corning, Calif., between U.S. Highway No. 99W and 99E when they saw what at first appeared to be a huge airliner dropping from the sky. This was at 11:50 P.M. They stopped and leaped from the patrol car in order to get a position on what they were sure was going to be an airplane crash. From their position outside the car the first thing they noticed was an absolute silence. Still assuming it to be an aircraft with power off, they continued to watch until the object was probably within 100 to 200 feet off the ground, whereupon it suddenly reversed completely, traveling at high speed back up the 45-degree glide path it had been taking, and gaining about 500-feet altitude.

This observation was from a distance of one-half to 1 mile. They said it was about the size of a DC-6 without wings; Officer Carson later made a sketch which shows an elliptical object 150 feet long and 40 feet high.

It was a very clear night, with no clouds, and as the object hovered for about a minute they got a good look at it. It was obviously not an aircraft of any design familiar to them, they said. It was surrounded by a white glow, making the object visible. At each end there were definite red lights, and at times five white lights were visible between the two red lights. They called the night dispatching office at the county sheriff's office and asked that other cars be sent, and that all other cars in the area be alerted. They also asked the radar base be notified.

The object then drifted westward toward them, losing altitude, and got within some 150 yards of them, easy pistol range, before drifting eastward again. During this time it performed aerial feats that seemed unbelievable. It was capable of moving in any direction—up, down, back, and forth. At times the movement was very slow, and at times completely motionless. It could move at extremely high speeds, and several times they watched it change direction or reverse itself while moving at unbelievable speeds.

As the object moved away from them toward the east, they followed at a judicial distance, encouraged by the expectation that they were to be joined by other officers. At that time they also radioed the Tehama County Sheriff's Office requesting that they contact the local radar base. By telephone the radar operator confirmed the UFO and stated that it was unidentified.

The two officers drove the next day to the local radar base, were refused permission to talk to the radar operator that had been on duty, and were given what Carson described as the "ice water treatment" by the commanding officer.

There follow many interesting details of their hide-and-seek chase with the object over the next 2 hours along the back roads of northern California, trying to get close enough to this thing to get a better observation. It seemed always to know they were there and always kept about half a mile away.

However, when we restrict our attention to the propulsion problem, the significant facts are: (1) there was no observable noise, (2) the UFO could hover—seemed to float as if it were in water—and move in any direction without altering its orientation, (3) it could sustain very high accelerations and move very rapidly, (4) it was able to hover or to move relatively slowly for at least 2 hours under circumstances that precluded suspension by aerodynamic lift forces.

What can we learn about the propulsion of UFO's from the information provided by the observations of these two police officers? Mainly, it is negative information. From the silence it seems impossible that it could have been supported by a jet or rocket reaction. There are further considerations involving specific impulse, energy, et cetera, that we need not go into here, that provide compelling arguments against any conventional way of counteracting the earth's gravitational field. There remains a slight possibility of developing sufficient reactive force by expelling relativistic neutrinos, for they would not be intercepted by the earth under a UFO and would not be noticed.

Expelling neutrons would have this same advantage, but in the quantities required they would induce far more radioactivity than has ever been measured at sites where UFO's have come close to the ground or have been reported to have landed.

Fortunately, there has been at least one observation that tends to provide a bit of positive information. Mr. Wells Allen Webb, an applied chemist with a master of science degree from the University of California, was 1 mile north of Spain Flying Field, 7 miles east of Yuma, Ariz., just off U.S. Highway No. 80, when his attention was drawn to the sky to the north by some low-flying jet aircraft. Then he noticed a small white cloud-like object in an otherwise cloudless sky.

He watched for about 5 minutes as it traveled eastward; as it reached a spot north-northeast of his location, it abruptly altered shape from being oblong and subtending about half the angle of the full moon—about 15 minutes of arc—to be circular and subtending about 5 minutes of arc. Webb was wearing polaroid glasses and noted that there appeared around the object a series of dark rings, the outermost of which was about six times the diameter of the central white or silvery object, or about the diameter of the full moon. The object or cloud then decreased in apparent diameter, as if it were traveling away from him, and disappeared in another few minutes. During this time Webb repeatedly took off his glasses and then put them back on, noting each time that the rings appeared only when he was wearing the glasses. He did not know what to make of the sighting, but took notes, including the fact that it was about 10 in the morning. The date was May 5, 1953.

One of the first things to note about the situation as described in the account is that the dark rings were observed with polaroid glasses, but not without them. The second thing is that, from the orientation of the observer relative to the position of the sun at that time of day, the blue scattered light from the part of the sky that formed the background for the object was polarized.

To this fortunate circumstance we must add the fact that Mr. Webb was curious about clouds, the effect of viewing them with polarized light, and took notes of what he observed. He did not, however, realize that he was observing the rotation of the plane of polarization of the blue light in the vicinity of the object. This was the interpretation I made some 8 years later upon reading his account.

Mr. WYDLER. How would you define UFO's as you are using it in this paper before us?

Dr. HARDER. I don't know how I could define it without being circular.

Mr. WYDLER. That is the conclusion to which I came.

You state on the very first page or you more or less say you are going to tacitly assume the reality of UFO's, merely an "unidentified flying object." I think we can assume their reality without worrying much about it. It is only if they have some particular interplanetary significance that might become a real problem, the way we look at it, isn't that so? We all agree there are unidentified flying objects.

I think you are defining them as interplanetary. I don't see you really come out and say that, but I think you hinted at it.

Dr. HARDER. Well, if my interpretation of these rings is correct, it is certainly nothing we have been able to accomplish on earth.

Mr. WYDLER. Are you saying, when you use this term, for the purposes of your statement, in your testimony, you are assuming they are of an interplanetary nature?

Dr. HARDER. Yes, that is right.

Mr. WYDLER. All right.

Dr. HARDER. In my statement, which is available to the transcriber, I have gone through a little bit of argument suggesting why the outer of the three rings represents light that had been rotated through 90 degrees, so it would not pass through the polarizer, if it is polarized glasses. The next ring represented light that had been rotated 90 plus 180 degrees. If you have polaroid glasses and look at the right part of the blue sky, any afternoon, you can see that the light is polarized, and as you rotate your polaroid glasses there is an alternate darkening-lightening, as you go through 180 degrees.

We can assume, to begin with, that the plane of the polarizer in his glasses was parallel to the plane of the undisturbed polarized light from the general direction of the object. If then something affected the light so as to turn its plane of polarization through 90 degrees, the portion that had been originally polarized would not pass through the glasses. Likewise, for light that had had its plane of polarization turned through 90 plus 180 degrees, 90 plus 360 degrees, and so on, there would be a partial extinction of light.

On this basis, the outer dark ring was due to the rejection by the polarizing filter of the glasses of light which had had its plane of polarization turned through 90 degrees, the next outermost band by light that had been turned through 270 degrees, et cetera.

This interpretation is strengthened by Webb's observation that the dark rings were narrower than the brighter areas between them; this is what should be expected on the basis of the above explanation.

What hypotheses can be constructed that might account for this unusual observation? There are at least two that have interesting implications for the propulsion problem. First by the Faraday effect, a magnetic field parallel to the path of the light could so rotate the plane of polarization. A quick calculation using the properties of the atmosphere shows that a field of 200,000 gauss, operating over a distance of 130 feet—40 meters—could turn the plane 90 degrees; this is indeed a very intense and extensive magnetic field and, of course, would only account for one ring. Three rings would require a million gauss over the same distance.

We have been able to achieve these field strengths in the laboratory for only fractions of seconds over very small distances. However, the principal argument against this hypothesis is the conclusion that were such a field brought at all close to the surface of the earth its effect would be to induce very strong remnant magnetism in nearly every piece of iron within several hundred yards. This has not been found.

We have been able to achieve that kind of field strength

for fractions of seconds only over short distances on earth, or at least we, on earth.

However, there has been a suggestion made earlier that a very strong magnetic field might so saturate certain iron cores of electrical machinery as to explain some of the observed phenomena of electrical malfunctioning.

Despite the above-described observation, there is little reason to believe that magnetic fields, of themselves, could be of much use in propelling a spacecraft, although there has been much uninformed speculation about this in popular UFO publications. The simple reason is that we cannot produce a north pole without at the same time producing a south pole. This a consequence of fundamental theory. Such a dipole cannot exert a force in conjunction with a uniform magnetic field, such as the earth may be assumed to have in a given locality, though it can produce a force in a nonuniform field.

To go beyond the above discussion would be rather speculative, but it is just here that we find a stimulus and challenge to scientific theory. It is almost circular to say that when we find a phenomenon we understand but vaguely we have also found a means of advancing our understanding; this has been particularly true in astronomy.

Concerning the propulsion of UFO's, a tentative hypothesis would be that it is connected with an application of gravitational fields that we do not understand.

Gravitation remains one of the enigmas of modern science, although there have been some advances in its understanding, beyond general relativity, in the past decade. There are theoretical grounds for believing there must exist a second gravitational field, corresponding to the magnetic field in electromagnetic theory, and that the interaction between these two fields must be similar to that between the electric and magnetic fields.

This interaction and its exploitation forms the basis for

our modern electrical generators and motors. Without the interaction, we would be back to the days of electrostatic attraction and of permanent magnets—two phenomena that can produce only very weak forces when operating individually. Some day perhaps we will learn enough to apply gravitational forces in the same way we have learned to apply electromagnetic forces. This will depend upon advances in many fields of science. Some of the things required will be enormously increased sources of power from atomic fusion; very intense magnetic fields and current densities, perhaps from superconducting sources; and extremely strong materials to contain mechanical forces. Some of these advances are approaching, or are on the horizon. Others we have yet to see clearly.

May I close this part of our discussion by recalling the statement that the most important secret of the atomic bomb was that it worked. This gave the crucial impetus to other nations in their own efforts to duplicate the research of the United States. In the UFO phenomena we have demonstrations of scientific secrets we do not know ourselves. It would be a mistake, it seems to me, to ignore their existence.

I have further comments on UFO's and high-strength materials, but perhaps the committee would rather interrupt at this point before I go on to that second subject?

Mr. ROUSH. Any questions?

I think you better go ahead, Dr. Harder, because if we get started questioning it is impossible to stop these people.

Mr. BOONE. Mr. Chairman, may I ask one question?

Mr. ROUSH. Go ahead, Mr. Boone.

Mr. BOONE. Have you concluded that what you have just told us is true, we should not ignore their existence?

Dr. HARDER. I have no doubt of the veracity of the observer who saw this thing in the sky; I know him personally.

Mr. BOONE. I didn't question the observer, I questioned

your remark, and the magnetic, if you will, electromagnetic interactions, and so forth, when you said we undoubtedly must admit the existence of these—I am sorry I can't quote you exactly. But your last sentence there is what I refer to.

It does seem like an obvious conclusion resulting from all the previous remarks you said about some supernatural, if you will——

Dr. HARDER. Oh, heavens, I never suggested that, I hope.

Mr. BOONE. Well, let me say, science fiction propulsion system, then.

Dr. HARDER. Well, sir, what we have been discussing this morning, and this afternoon, is perhaps closer to science fiction than anything. I hope it is more science than fiction, however.

Mr. ROUSH. Go ahead, Dr. Harder.

Dr. HARDER. The instances in which physical fragments of UFO's have been found are disappointingly few. To my knowledge, there is only one well-authenticated finding, and that was in Brazil, in 1957. The story of its discovery is contained in chapter 9 of the Great Flying Saucer Hoax, written by Dr. Olavo T. Fontes.

Briefly, several small metallic fragments were recovered by some fishermen near the coastal town of Ubatuba, Sao Paulo, after they saw what they described as a brilliant explosion of a flying disc. Some of the fiery fragments were extinguished in the water near the shore, where they were recovered.

Fontes acquired three of the fragments that weighed less than a tenth of an ounce each, and had one of them analyzed at the Mineral Production Laboratory in the Brazilian Agriculture Ministry. The results of the first analysis [were] that the substance was magnesium of an unusually high degree of purity, and that there was an absence of any other metallic element.

On the basis of the first examination a second spectrographic test was conducted, using the utmost care and the most modern instruments.

The second report was again marked by references to the "extreme purity" of the sample. Even impurities that are sometimes detected due to contamination from the carbon rod used as an electrode were absent. A further test, using X-ray diffraction, failed to turn up any other metallic component.

One of the pieces was flown to California and was analyzed. I have the report here. They used neutron activation analysis and discovered a total of one-tenth of 1 percent of other metallic elements than magnesium, 500 parts per million zinc, that included zinc, which is interesting, and small amounts of barium and strontium.

Certainly this metal is of extraordinary purity, certainly far beyond the capacity of fishermen at Ubatuba to produce.

What could be the use of such high-purity magnesium in the context of a spacecraft? One clue lies in its crystalline structure. It is close packed hexagonal structure, and is in this regard similar to the high-strength metals beryllium and titanium. Hexagonal crystals have but one slip plane, and this tends to make them brittle but strong.

One of the reasons for slip along crystal planes is that local imperfections in the crystal, or foreign atoms, create lines of stress concentration that move rapidly through the crystal, producing deformation.

If these imperfections, or dislocations, could be eliminated, the theoretical strength of the crystal lattice itself might be approached. This strength is on the order of millions of pounds per square inch for any materials. Carefully prepared ¼-inch diameter glass rods, etched to remove microscopic surface cracks and then laquered, have withstood stress of 250,000 psi for 1 hour. Fused silica fibers have been stressed to 2 million psi.

Thus, foreign atoms within a crystal lattice are focal points for dislocations—points of stress concentration where the crystal lattice itself tears and slips. We can imagine that a high-purity crystal, free of surface and internal imperfections, would achieve fantastic strengths. Indeed, with the advent of iron whiskers, and boron fiber reinforced composites, we are already approaching some of these strengths, but only for extremely small diameter fibers.

Should, by any good fortune, further samples of UFO material be found, there may be further clues that would spur on research into high-strength materials, and perhaps give us hints of how to achieve superstrength in materials that are larger than the tiny fibers we have produced so far.

Needless to say, if we persist in denying the reality of UFO's we will not be looking for such samples, and may indeed reject them as having no importance when they are brought to our attention.

That is the conclusion of my prepared statement. I would like to comment on some of the suggestions as asked by Congressman Rumsfeld earlier.

I conclude in some of my colleagues' recommendations that a multiple-faceted exploration be made of this subject, preferably at several institutions simultaneously.

I have some suggestions as to how we could acquire additional scientific data even at the present time.

This is a three-point program which involves first the establishment of an early warning network, which the Colorado project began last February. Then to take advantage of one of the characteristics of UFO sightings: that they, in many instances, are seen on one or two successive nights.

We could have prearranged instrument packages which are arranged for instant transportation to locations where UFO's have been sighted. If the budget for such a program were low, you might be able to borrow such things and have them ready at various universities where the instruments were otherwise occupied for research.

That would be the second point of this investigation.

The third point would be the cooperation of the Air Force for logistics and high-speed transport to crucial areas on a 24-hour basis.

Now, that three-point program may well bring to us physical data that so far has appeared only in anecdotal, still from essential amateurs who happened just accidentally to be at the right place. It was truly a fortunate accident when Mr. Webb was there to make the observation I described earlier.

Mr. ROUSH. Does that conclude your statement?

Dr. HARDER. That concludes my statement.

Dr. Harder's comments began by pointing the finger toward a reason that could explain Dr. Condon's recalcitrant attitude in facing the mystifying positive aspects of his staff's research. The extraterrestrial hypothesis does, as Dr. Harder said, tend to undermine the collective ego of the human race. While his comment had nothing directly to do with Dr. Condon, this potential diminution of human talents could understandably provoke many scientists to look the other way in the face of very strong and even overpowering evidence. Dr. Harder admits he has been affected by this thought, although he recognizes that it has no place in the scientific assessment of facts.

He also brings up the essential point that by ordinary rules of evidence, the physical reality of UFO's has been proved beyond a reasonable doubt. If this is true—and the statement almost *has* to be accepted as true—what motivates the reluctance of many to accept it? The ego factor is only one element. Fear is another, in spite of the lack of evidence of UFO hostility, and the presence of evidence that many witnesses have reacted more with curiosity than with panic. I am speaking now of accepting the physical reality of UFOs as true, not of an explanation as to what they are. It is true that the scientific data (radar-visual fixes, electromagnetic effects on cars, reasonably verified photographs, animal reactions) are not strong, but they do exist. The question is why this raw material is totally dismissed by Dr. Condon and others instead of being the springboard for intensive further study in the face of the striking evidence at hand. No intelligent person claims that UFOs are scientifically established. He might claim that, with the physical reality of them being proved by the rules of evidence, the scientific proof must then logically be sought and found. In contrast, Condon simply calls for the dismissal of the subject.

The multiple-witness, long-duration, radar-confirmed sighting, characterized by radio interference, as detailed by Dr. Harder, is important because it is typical of so many cases recorded by police, pilots, and radar men that are begging for adequate explanation. A cursory brush-off of cases like these involving articulate witnesses and radar confirmation can only be regarded as inexcusable arrogance. Further, it is an indirect accusation that the officers and other witnesses are either totally incompetent, total liars, or totally deluded. Yet case after case like these are being ignored by the Air Force and Dr. Condon, to say nothing of journalistic commentators like Walter Sullivan of *The New York Times*. They seem to assume an unjustified pose of Olympian grandeur while they condescendingly explain how deluded the officers who make a sighting like this are. I would feel much more comfortable about Mr. Sullivan and Dr. Condon if they put on hip boots and literally followed through cases like these on the scene, but there is no evidence of their ever having done so. The odd part is that competent scientists like many of those who testified at the Congressional hearings did do just that, and changed from an attitude of skepticism to one of considerable puzzlement. Anyone who permits himself to be frozen in his attitude toward such a widespread phenomenon must be forced to admit a lack of comprehension, both scientific and common. It might be as interesting, as a matter of fact, to psychologically analyze the viewpoint of those who totally refuse to accept *rational and articulate evidence*, just as they recommend psychological analysis of those people who have reported UFO sightings. Those on either extreme might be equally suspect. Resistance to *reasonable* evidence is often as pathological as total gullibility.

Dr. Harder's comments on possible propulsion have to remain in the speculation arena, but the cases he presents to indicate the type of nonaerodynamic behavior of well-documented UFO sightings are persuasively indicative of power systems far beyond our capacity. It seems that the main problem remains to convince the recalcitrant scientist to ignore the Condon conclusions so that all aspects of the UFO can be sought and discovered, with the propulsion system being one of several critical questions to be answered. Dr. Harder, in attempting to explore this question, is searching in murky seas. But he is pointing out rationally documented imponderables that should be given attention if any progress is to be made. His prepared statement filed with his testimony examines the technical aspect of propulsion and high-strength material in considerable detail, and offers areas of possible further exploration.

# 6.

DR. Robert M. L. Baker, Jr., the next scientist to testify, has been a consultant to the Douglas Aircraft Company, former head of Lockheed's Astrodynamics Research Center, project officer on a number of classified Air Force projects, and is presently a senior scientist with the Computer Sciences Corporation. His academic background includes a Ph.D. in engineering from UCLA, one of the first degrees of its kind to be granted with a specialty in astronautics. He has been on the faculty of UCLA in the departments of both astronomy and engineering, and currently teaches astronautics, fluid mechanics, and structural mechanics there in addition to his other work. His scientific work is internationally recognized. He has been editor of the *Journal of Astronautical Sciences* since 1963, as well as National Chairman of the Astrodynamics Technical Committee of the American Institute of Aeronautics and Astronautics.

His interest in UFOs began, he relates in his testimony, with the study of two short UFO film clips while he was a consultant for Douglas Aircraft. After some eighteen months of detailed analysis of the films he came to the conclusion that in this and several other film UFO cases, natural phenomena were not a source for the images. In other words, the sightings and films were impossible to explain in normal terms.

His testimony regarding the fact that some of the major

scientific tracking systems and astronomical optical systems have shown anomalistic inexplicable data is most important. In addition, he points out that other space surveillance systems are simply not set up to track the erratic motions of such objects as UFOs. Only one partially classified tracking system, he feels, has even a slight opportunity for continuous and effective coverage, and since that sensor system has been in operation, there have been a number of alarms that have *not* been explained by natural causes, faulty equipment, or man-made space objects.

Dr. Baker takes issue with the theories of Menzel and Klass, and is convinced that in the photographs he has personally analyzed, their explanations are simply not valid.

Dr. Baker's recommendations are based on sound reasoning and acute awareness of the difficulties involved in solving the problem. His supplementary material is detailed, painstaking, and extensive. But his expert attempt to correct the misconception about instrumental infallibility that so many people have is his most important contribution as far as the lay reader is concerned. As he states clearly in his testimony, "We have not now, nor have we been in the past, able to achieve a complete—or even partially complete—surveillance of space in the vicinity of the earth, comprehensive enough to betray the presence of, or provide quantitative information on, anomalistic phenomena."

With this in mind, the testimony that follows is of particular interest.

Dr. Baker. Thank you, Mr. Roush.

I should like to preface my remarks by stating my preference for the term "anomalistic observational phenomena," as opposed to the term "unidentified flying objects."

Mr. Roush. I observed you were going to say that and I wonder about some of my Hoosiers back home using those terms.

Dr. BAKER. It comes trippingly off the tongue.

Mr. ROUSH. It might not only cause some Hoosiers but some laymen some problems. It might be easier to say UFO's. You may go ahead.

Dr. BAKER. I call it AOP.

From the data I have reviewed and analyzed since 1954, it is my belief that there does exist substantial evidence to support the claim that an unexplained phenomenon—or phenomena—is present in the environs of the earth, but that it may not be "flying," may not always be "unidentified," and, perhaps, may not even be substantive "objects." In the following statement I will—

> (1) Present a summary of the analyses I have accomplished to date—those that have led me to believe that anomalistic phenomena exist;
>
> (2) Explain the probable inadequacy of our current terrestrial sensors in observing and/or defining the characteristics of the anomalistic phenomena;
>
> (3) Suggest a number of tentative hypothetical sources for the phenomena, and the justification for their scientific study;
>
> (4) And, finally, I will make specific recommendations concerning the necessity for new types of closely related observational and study programs which might be implemented in a fashion that would permit the detection and quantitative analysis of the anomalistic phenomena.

Several appendixes accompany this report. The first two are in response to Congressman Roush's invitational letter of July 10, 1968, and consist of my biographical sketch and a listing of my bibliography, respectively. The third appendix relates directly to my specific recommendations, and was included with the kind permission of Dr. Sydney

Walker III. The fourth appendix presents three reprints of articles (Baker (1968a) and (1968b) and Walker (1968)) that are pertinent to the subject matter of this report.

My initial contact with anomalistic observational phenomena—AOP—came in 1954 when I was a consultant to Douglas Aircraft Co. in Santa Monica, Calif., serving as special assistant to Dr. W. B. Klemperer, director of Douglas' research staff. The data consisted of two short film clips: one taken in Montana—termed by us as the Montana film—and one taken in Utah—called by us the Utah film. These films were provided to us by the Air Technical Intelligence Center—ATIC, now the Foreign Technology Division—FTD—at Wright-Patterson Air Force Base; 35-millimeter prints were furnished by Green-Rouse Productions of Samuel Goldwyn Studios.

Both films had been taken by apparently reliable and unbiased men using amateur movie cameras and, in each case, there was a credible, substantiating witness present. The films exhibited the motion of rather fuzzy white dots, but the Montana film was remarkable in that foreground was visible on most of the frames.

Preliminary analysis excluded most natural phenomena. More detailed study indicated that the only remaining natural phenomenon candidate for the Utah film was birds in flight, and for the Montana film it was airplane fuselage reflections of the sun. After about 18 months of rather detailed, albeit not continuous, study using various film-measuring equipment at Douglas and at UCLA, as well as analysis of a photogrammetric experiment, it appeared that neither of these hypothesized natural phenomena explanations had merit, and a report was published by me (Baker [1956])and forwarded to Brig. Gen. Harold E. Watson, commander, ATIC. Since the description of the circumstances of the filmings and the analyses of the data provided on the films is rather lengthy, and have since been published in the open literature, it does not seem unreasonable to repeat the analyses here.

During the course of this study we also had the opportunity to view some gun-camera photographs taken over Florida. Unfortunately, we could not retain this film, and did not have time available to accomplish a comprehensive analysis. Like the Montana and Utah films, this film also exhibited only white-dot images; however, since a foreground was present, a competent study could have been carried out. Dr. Klemperer and I agreed on the preliminary conclusion—not supported by detailed analyses—that, again, no natural phenomenon was a likely source for the images.

In June of 1963 I received a movie film clip from a Mr. Richard Hall that had purportedly been taken from an aircraft (DC-3) near Angel Falls, Venezuela, at about 12:15 P.M. This film clip was 8-millimeter color film, exposed at 16 frames per second and showed a very bright yellow, slightly pear-shaped object that disappeared in a cloud bank after about 60 or 70 frames. At the time I was the head of the Lockheed Aircraft Co.'s Astrodynamics Research Center. We had developed a small group of photogrammetrist consisting of Dr. P. M. Merifeld and Mr. James Rammellkamp, and were able to undertake a study of the film. Initially, Merifeld and Rammellkamp found little of interest on the film. After their preliminary examination, I expended considerable effort in further analysis. Again, I was only able to draw the conclusion that the yellow object was no known natural phenomenon; but we could make a quantitative determination of angular rates and accelerations, and the bounds of distance, linear velocity, and acceleration, the film was lost (except for a mocrophotograph exhibiting the object on one frame). There was, however, no question in my mind as to the anomalistic character of the images.

In January 1964, Mr. Zan Overall showed me three cinetheodolite films which had been taken simultaneously by three different cameras of a Thor-Able Star launching at Vandenberg AFB (project A4/01019). These films depicted a white object moving vertically (relative to the film frame) against a clear, blue-sky background. The object was about as bright as the booster's second-stage exhaust, and passed the booster at about one-third degree per second. Rough estimates of the direction of the Sun—based on shadows on early frames—and the winds aloft—indicated by the motion of the rocket's exhaust plume—were made. These, together with the brightness of the object and its rate of ascent, seemed to rule out balloons, airplanes, lens flare, mirages, et cetera. Since one of the cinetheodolites was at a site some distance from the other two, a parallax determination of the actual distance and speed of the object could be determined rather easily. Because the films were on loan from the Navy, I was unable to carry out the necessary study and a determination of the precise character of the phenomenon (natural or anomalistic) could not be made. In 1967, I discussed the matter with Prof. William K. Hartmann of the University of Arizona, and Prof. Roy Craig of the University of Colorado. At that time, they were involved in the Colorado UFO Study Group, and indicated that they would attempt to obtain the film for further analysis. Although I am confident that they made a conscientious effort to obtain the films, apparently they were unsuccessful (as of 6 months ago, at least).

In addition to the foregoing film clips—which seemed to involve data that were the result of anomalistic phenomena —the Montana film in my opinion, certainly was anomalistic and all of the other films except for the California film, most probably were anomalistic—I have also had the opportunity to view approximately a half dozen other films, purportedly of "UFO's." The images on these films appeared possibly to be the result of natural phenomena, such as reflections on airplanes, atmospheric mirages, optical flares, birds, balloons, insects, satellites, et cetera. For example, a recent (February 1968) set of two films were taken, using professional motion picture equipment, by a Universal Studio crew on location. Although rather peculiar in appearance, the objects thus photographed could have conceivably been the result of airplane reflections.

To this date my analyses of anomalistic motion picture data have been rather ungratifying. Although I am convinced that many of the films indeed demonstrated the presence of anomalistic phenomena, they all have the characteristic of rather ill-defined blobs of light, and one can actually gain little insight into the real character of the phenomena. For example, linear distance, speed, and acceleration cannot be determined precisely, nor can size and mass. As I will discuss in a moment, this situation is not particularly surprising, since, without a special-purpose sensor system expressly designed to obtain information pertinent to anomalistic observational phenomena, or a general-purpose sensor system operated so as not to disregard such data, the chance for obtaining high-quality hard data is quite small.

The capabilities of astronomical optical sensors have been dealt with in a thorough fashion by Page in 1968. The Prairie Network for Meteor Observations (McCrosky and Posen (1968)) is a good example of a wide-coverage optical system, but as is so often the case, and as Page (1968) pointed out. ". . . R. E. McCrosky of the Smithsonian Astrophysical Observatory informed me that no thorough search (for anomalistic data) has been carried out." Even so, some astronomical photographs are bound to exhibit anomalistic data. Again quoting from Page (1968), ". . . W. T. Powers of Northwestern University Astronomy Department informed me that 'several' of the Smithsonian-net

photographs show anomalous trails." As I have already
pointed out (Baker (1968b) to be found in appendix 4),
the majority of our astronomical equipment (e.g., conventional photographic telescopes, Baker-Nunn cameras, meteor cameras, Markowitz Dual-rate Moon Cameras, et
cetera) are special purpose in nature, and would probably
not detect the anomalous luminous phenomena reported
by the casual observer if they were indeed present. Their
photographic speed, field of view, et cetera, impose severe
restrictions on their ability to collect data on objects other
than those they have been specifically designed to detect.
As already noted in the quotes from Page (1968), even if
such data were collected, the recognition of their unique-
ness or anomalous character by an experimenter is improbable. Examples abound, in the history of celestial
mechanics, of minor planets being detected on old astronomical plates that had been measured for other purposes,
and then abandoned.

Our radar and optical space surveillance and tracking
systems are even more restrictive and thus, even less likely
to provide information on anomalistic phenomena than are
astronomical sensors. The Signal Test Processing Facility
(STPF) radar at Floyd, N.Y. is a high-performance experimental radar having a one-third degree beam width. For
lockon and track, an object would have to be pinpointed to
one-sixth degree, and even if the radar did achieve lockon,
an erratically moving object could not be followed even in
the STPF radar's monopulse mode of operation. For this
reason only satellites having rather well-defined paths (i.e.,
ephemerides), which have been precomputed, can be acquired and tracked.

Our three BEMEWS radars propagate fans of electromagnetic energy into space. If a ballistic missile or satellite
penetrates two of these fans successively, then it can be

identified. Since astrodynamical laws govern the time interval between detection fan penetrations for "normal" space objects, all other anomalistic "hits" by the radar are usually neglected, and even if they are not neglected, they are usually classified as spurious images or misassociated targets, and are stored away on magnetic tape, and forgotten.

One space surveillance site operates a detection radar (FPS-17) and a tracking radar (FPS-79). If a new space object is sensed by the detection radar's fans, then the tracking radar can be oriented to achieve lockon. The orientation is governed by a knowledge of the appropriate "normal" object's astrodynamic laws of motion, or by an assumption as to launch point. Thus, if an unknown is detected, and if it follows an unusual path, it is unlikely that it could, or would, be tracked. Furthermore, the director of the radar may make a decision that the unknown object detected is not of interest (because of the location of the FPS-17 fan penetration or because of the lack of prior information on a possible new launch). In the absence of detection fan penetration (the fan has a rather limited coverage), the FPS-79 tracking radar is tasked to follow other space objects on a schedule provided by the Space Defense Center, and again there is almost no likelihood that an anomalistic object could, or would, be tracked.

The NASA radars, such as those at Millstone and Goldstone, are not intended to be surveillance radars, and only track known space objects on command. Again the chances of their tracking anomalistic objects are nearly nil. The new phased-array radar at Eglin AFB (FPS-85) has considerable capability for deploying detection fans and tracking space objects in a simultaneous fashion. Such versatility raises certain energy-management problems—that is, determining how much energy to allocate to detection and how much to tracking—but this sensor might have a capability (albeit, perhaps, limited) to detect and track anomalistic objects. The problem is that the logic included in the software associated with the FPS-85's control computers is not organized in a fashion to detect and track anomalistic objects (I will indicate in a moment how the logic could be modified). Furthermore, the FPS-85, like the other surveillance radars is usually tasked to track a list of catalogued space objects in the Space Defense Center's data base and the opportunity to "look around" for anomalistic objects is quite limited.

There are a number of other radar surveillance systems such as a detection fence across the United States. In the case of this fence, we have a situation similar to BMEWS, in which the time interval between successive penetrations (in this case separated by an orbital period for satellites) must follow prescribed astrodynamical laws. If they do not, then the fence penetrations are either deleted from the data base or classified as "unknowns," or "uncorrelated targets," filed, and forgotten.

There is only one surveillance system, known to me, that exhibits sufficient and continuous coverage to have even a slight opportunity of betraying the presence of anomalistic phenomena operating above the Earth's atmosphere. The system is partially classified and, hence, I cannot go into great detail at an unclassified meeting. I can, however, state that yesterday (July 28, 1968) I traveled to Colorado Springs (location of the Air Defense Command) and confirmed that since this particular sensor system has been in operation, there have been a number of anomalistic alarms. Alarms that, as of this date, have not been explained on the basis of natural phenomena interference, equipment malfunction or inadequacy, or manmade space objects.

In Baker and Makemson (1967), I discussed the usual candidates for the natural sources of anomalistic observations. For example, some scanning radars—such as airport radars—pick up anomalistic returns termed "angels." A variety of explanations have been proposed, variously involving ionized air inversion layers, etc. (see Tacker (1960)) and even insects (see Glover, et al. (1966)). With respect to human observation of anomalistic luminous phenomena, some rather strong positions have been taken by such authorities as Menzel (1953), who feels that the predominant natural phenomenon is atmospheric mirages; by Klass (1958a), who feels that the predominant natural phenomenon is related to ball lightning triggered by high-tension line coronal discharge, jet aircraft, electrical storms, etc.; by Robey (1960), who feels that the observations are of "cometoids" entering the earth's atmosphere, etc. The list of hypothetical sources for anomalistic observational phenomena is long indeed, but from the photographic data that I have personally analyzed, I am convinced that none of these explanations is valid.

The analyses that I have carried out to date have dealt with observational evidence that I term "hard data"—that is, permanent photographic data. Although I will not discuss in detail the analyses of eyewitness reports (which I term "soft data"), Powers (1967), McDonald (1967), Hynek (1966), and others have concluded that overwhelming evidence exists that a truly anomalistic phenomenon is present.

Of course, there are numerous others who have come to a completely opposite conclusion; in fact, it becomes almost a matter of personal preference: it is possible for one to identify all of the anomalistic data as very unusual manifestations of natural phenomena. No matter how unlikely it is, anything is possible—even a jet plane reflecting the sun in direct opposition to the laws of optics. I'm sometimes reminded of the flat earth debates that I organized 10 years ago in my elementary astronomy courses at UCLA. Some students became so involved in justifying their positions—either flat or spherical—that they would grasp at even the most improbable argument in order to rationalize their stand.

Personally, I feel that it is premature for me to agree that the hard and soft data forces the scientific community to give overriding attention to the hypothesis that the anomalistic observations arise from manifestations of extraterrestrial beings. On the other hand, I strongly advocate the establishment of a research program in the area of anomalistic phenomena—an interdisciplinary research effort that progresses according to the highest scientific standards; that is well funded; and that is planned to be reliably long term. The potential benefit of such a research project to science should not hinge solely on the detection of intelligent extraterrestrial life; it should be justified by the possibility of gaining new insights into poorly understood phenomena, such as ball lightning, cometoid impact, and spiraling meteorite decay.

There is practical value in such research for the Military Establishment, as well. Let us suppose that something similar to the "Tunguska event" of 1908 occurred today, and that it was Long Island in the United States, rather than the Podkamenaia Tunguska River Basin in Siberia that was devastated by a probable comet impact. Would we misinterpret this catastrophic event as the signal for World War III? What if another "fireball procession," such as occurred over Canada on February 9, 1913, repeated itself today, and the low-flying meteors were on nearly polar orbits that would overfly the continental United States. Would we interpret the resulting surveillance data as indicating that a fractional orbital bombardment system (FOBS) had been initiated in Russia? My knowledge of our Air Force sensors, both current and projected (see Baker and Ford (1968)), indicates that they are sufficiently sophisticated so that they would probably not react prematurely and signal a false alarm—although a careful study of this point should be made. On the other hand, there may exist other anomalistic sources of data that might give rise to a false alarm and perhaps provoke us either to deploy our countermeasures, or even to counterattack.

Before I enumerate the specific benefits this research might confer upon various scientific disciplines, allow me to digress briefly on the subject of soft data. The primary reason that I have avoided the introduction of soft data into my photographic studies and have not involved myself in the analysis of eyewitness reports (such as the excellent ones given by Fuller (1966)), is that I have been unable to develop a rational basis for determining the credibility level for any given human observer. Although they lie outside the field of my own scientific competence, I feel that credibility evaluations of witnesses would form an important adjunct to any serious study of anomalistic phenomena (see Walker (1968) included in app. 4 of this report). The soft data must involve some useful information content, and it would be extremely unrealistic to neglect it entirely. For this reason, I have included appendix 3 by Dr. Walker, which presents a logical procedure for establishing a credibility level for observers. Walker's report of a hypothetical case integrates the results of general medical, neuroophthalmologic, neurologic, and psychiatric evaluations, and develops a logical basis for assigning an overall credibility score.

Dr. Robert L. Hall is, of course, eminently qualified to comment on the question of eyewitness testimony at this seminar.

If serious studies can be initiated, with the objectives of detecting, analyzing, and identifying the sources of anomalistic observational phenomena, then I feel that the following scientific benefits can be expected:

(1) *Meteoritics.*—Although there are a number of excellent meteor observation nets operating today, data col-

lected on erratically moving phenomena (including rapid determination of the location of any "landings" or impacts) would add significantly to the coverage and analyses of meteorites and, possibly, entering comets. Furthermore, the timely recovery of meteoritic debris at the subend point of fireballs would be most valuable.

(2) *Geology.*—It has been pointed out by Lamar and Baker (1965), that there exist residual effects on desert pavements that may have been produced by entering comets. Furthermore, any geological or material evidence of the impact or "landing" of extraterrestrial objects would be of great interest. As Dr. John O'Keefe (1967), Assistant Chief, Laboratory for Theoretical Studies of NASA GSFC indicated "Would it not be possible to get some scraps of these ("UFO") objects for examination? For instance, a scrap of matter, however small, could be analyzed for the kind of alloys in terrestrial foundries.

A piece of a screw, however small, would be either English, Metric, or Martian. I am impressed by this because I looked at some tens of thousands of pictures of the Moon and found that the very small amount of chemical data has more weight in interpreting the past history of the Moon than the very large amount of optical data. It doesn't seem possible that objects ("flying saucers") of this size can visit the Earth and then depart, leaving nothing, not even a speck, behind. We could analyze a speck no bigger than a pinhead very easily." I concur with O'Keefe's remarks, and if there exist "landings" associated with the anomalistic phenomena, then a prompt and extremely thorough investigation of the landing site must be accomplished before geological/material evidence is dispersed or terrestrialized.

(3) *Atmospheric physics.*—One of the great mysteries today is the formation, movement, and explosion of ball lightning. As Singer (1963) noted:

The specific properties of ball lightning, which present particular difficulty in experimental duplication, are formations of the sphere in air (at near-atmospheric pressure and at a distance from the source of energy) and its extensive motion. It is evident that additional clarification of both theoretical and experimental aspects is needed.

With respect to "plasma UFO's" Mr. Philip J. Klass (1968b) comments that:

If conditions—all of the conditions—needed to create plasma-UFO's near high-tension lines or in the wake of jet aircraft occurred readily we should have millions of UFO reports and the mystery would have been solved long ago. But the comparative rarity of legitimate UFO sightings clearly indicates that the ball-lightning related phenomenon is a very rare one.

Even if ball lightning is not the primary source of anomalistic data (and I am not at present convinced that it is), any program investigating anomalistic observational phenomena would surely shed significant light on the ball-lightning problem.

(4) *Astronomy.*—I have already noted the possibility of cometary entry, a study of which would be valuable to the astronomer. If as some respected astronomers believe, the anomalistic observational phenomena (including perhaps, "intelligent" radio signals from interstellar space) are the results of an advanced extraterrestrial civilization, then the study of the phenomena would become a primary concern of the entire human race. The implications for astronomy are overwhelming.

(5) *Psychiatry and psychology.*—Since bizarre events have been reported, the study of eyewitness credibility, under stressful circumstances of visual input, is possible. As I will recommend later: if a competent, mobile task force

of professionals could be sent into action as soon as anomalistic events are detected, then reliable evaluation of eyewitness reports (soft data) in relation to the actual hard
data obtained, could be accomplished. Even if the event was
only a spectacular fireball, or marsh gas, the psychiatric/
medical examination of eyewitnesses would still be more
informative.

(6) *Social science.*—Although not classified as a physical
science, there appears to be a challenge here for the social
sciences. It has been my contention throughout this report
that it is not a prerequisite to the study of anomalistic observational phenomena to suppose that they result from extraterrestrial intelligence.

Nevertheless, it still is an open possibility in my mind. It
seems reasonable, therefore, to undertake a few contingency
planning studies. In order to extract valuable information
from an advanced society, it would seem useful to forecast
the approximate characteristics of such a superior intelligence—or, if not necessarily superior, an intelligence displayed by an industrial, exploratory culture of substantially
greater antiquity. There exist dozens of treatises on technological forecasting; one can key estimates of technological
advancement to speed of travel, production of energy,
productivity, ubiquity of communications, etc. There have
been many debates on the technical capabilities or limits
on the capabilities of advanced extraterrestrial societies (for
example, see Markowitz (1967) and Rosa, et al. (1967)).
Often intermixed with these technological capabilities arguments, however, are very dubious comments concerning
the psychological motivations, behavioral patterns, and un-
based projections of the social motivations of an advanced
society. Hypothetical questions are often raised such as,
"* * * if there are flying saucers around, why don't they
contact us directly? * * * I would if I were investigating
another civilization." Such comments are made on ex-

tremely thin ice, for, to my knowledge, no concerted study has been carried out in the area of forecasting the social characteristics of an advanced extraterrestrial civilization. Philosophers, social scientists, and others usually undertake studies of rather theoretical problems. (See Wooldridge (1968) and Minas and Ackoff (1964).) If only a quantitative index or indices of social advancement could be developed that, say, would differentiate us from the Romans in our interpersonal and intersociety relationships (for example, tendencies toward fewer crimes of violence, fewer wars, etc.), then we might be better equipped to make rational extrapolations from our own to an advanced society. In fact, such an index, if it could be developed, might even be beneficial in guiding our existing earth-based society.

(7) *Serendipity.*—In addition to the value of anomalistic phenomena studies to these specific scientific disciplines, there is always serendipity. Any scientific study of this nature is potentially capable of giving substantial dividends in terms of "spin-off." For example: in improved techniques in radar and optical sensor design and control; in giving a reliable quantitative credibility level to witness' statements in court; or in deciphering and/or analyzing anomalistic radio signals from interstellar space.

For the past 16 years I have seriously (albeit sporadically) followed the analyses of "UFO" or "flying saucer" reports—both scientific and quasi-scientific. It is my conclusion that there is only so much quantitative data that we can squeeze out of vast amounts of data on anomalistic observational phenomena that has been collected to date. I believe that we will simply frustrate ourselves by endless arguments over past, incomplete data scenarios; what we need is more sophisticated analyses of fresh anomalistic observational data. We must come up with more than just a rehash of old data.

I emphasize that it is very unlikely that existing optical and radar monitoring systems would collect the type of quantitative data that is required to identify and study the phenomena. Moreover, we currently have no quantitative basis upon which to evaluate and rank (according to credibility) the myriad of eyewitness reports. Thus continuing to "massage" past anomalistic events would seem to be a waste of our scientific resources. In balance, then, I conclude that:

(1) We have not now, nor have we been in the past, able to achieve a complete—or even partially complete—surveillance of space in the vicinity of the earth, comprehensive enough to betray the presence of, or provide quantitative information on, anomalistic phenomena.

(2) Hard data on anomalistic observational phenomena do, in fact exist, but they are of poor quality, because of the inadequacies of equipment employed in obtaining them.

(3) Soft data on anomalistic phenomena also exist, but we have no quantitative procedure to evaluate their credibility and develop clear-cut conclusions on the characteristics of the anomalistic phenomena.

(4) It follows from the scientific method that an experiment or experiments should be devised, and closely related study programs be initiated expressly to define the anomalistic data better.

(5) In order to justify such an experiment and associated studies, it is not necessary to presuppose the existence of intelligent extraterrestrial life operating in the environs of the earth, or to make dubious speculations either concerning "their" advanced scientific and engineering capabilities or "their" psychological motivations and behavioral patterns.

In the light of these conclusions, I will make the following recommendations:

(1) In order to obtain information-rich hard and soft data on anomalistic phenomena, an interdisciplinary, mobile task force or team of highly qualified scientists should be organized. This team should be established on a long-term basis, well funded, and equipped to swing into action and investigate reports on anomalistic phenomena immediately after such reports are received. Because of the relatively low frequency of substantive reports . . . immediate results should not be anticipated, but in the interim periods between their investigations in the field, their time could be productively spent in making thorough analyses of data collected by them previously, and in "sharpening up" their analysis tools.

(2) In concert with the aforementioned task force, a sensor system should be developed expressly for detecting and recording anomalistic observational phenomena for hard-data evaluation. The system might include one or more phased-array radars (certainly not having the cost or capability of the FPS-85, but operating in a limited fashion that would be similar to the FPS-85). A phased-array radar would have the advantage over a conventional "dish" radar in that it could track at high rates and divide its energy in an optimum fashion between detection and tracking. The control system would be unique, and would necessitate the development of a sequential data-processing controller that would increase the state variables describing the object's path from a six-dimensional position and velocity estimation to a 12-dimensional acceleration and jerk estimation (Baker (1967)) in order to follow erratic motion.

In addition, the data base would have to be especially designed, to avoid manmade space objects and (if possible) airplanes, birds, common meteors, etc. It should, however, be designed to detect and track nearby cometoids, macrometeorites (fireballs), ball lightning, and any other erratic or anomalistic object within its range. Optical cameras (including spectrographic equipment) should be slaved to the radar, in order to provide more comprehensive data. Because of the aforementioned low frequency of anomalistic data, alarms from the system should not occur very frequently and could be communicated directly to the recommended task force.

(3) A proposed new-generation, space-based long-wavelength infrared surveillance sensor system should be funded and the associated software should be modified to include provisions for the addition of anomalistic objects in its data base. The specific sensor system cannot be identified for reasons of security, but details can probably be obtained from the Air Force. This sensor system, in particular, could provide some data (perhaps incomplete) on anomalistic objects which exhibit a slight temperature contrast with the space background, on a basis of noninterference with its military mission. The system represents a promising technological development, and no other novel technique introduced in recent years offers more promise for space surveillance. In my view, the scientific principles underlying the proposed surveillance system are sound, and a developmental measurements program should be initiated.

(4) The software designed for the FPS-85 phase-array radar at Eglin Air Force Base be extended in order to provide a capability to detect and track anomalistic space objects. The relatively inexpensive modification could include the implementation of tracking techniques such as those outlined in Baker (1967). It should, however, be clearly borne in mind that only a limited amount of tracking time (about 30 percent) could be devoted to this endeavor, because of the overriding importance of the surveillance of manmade space objects which is the basic responsibility of this radar.

(5) Various "listening post" projects should be reestablished (using existing instruments) in order to seek out pos-

sible communications from other intelligent life sources in the universe. See, for example, Shklovskii and Sagan (1966), chapters 27, 28, 30, and 34.

(6) Technological and behavioral pattern forecasting studies should be encouraged in order to give at least limited insight into the gross characteristics of an advanced civilization. These studies (probably not Government funded) should include the social-psychological implications of anomalistic observational phenomena, as well as the psychological impact upon our own culture that could be expected from "contact" with an advanced civilization. (See ch. 33 of Shklovskii and Sagan (1966).)

(7) Studies should be initiated in the psychiatric/medical problems of evaluating the credibility of witness' testimony concerning bizarre or unusual events. (See app. 3 of this report.)

All of the foregoing recommendations involve the expenditure of funds, and we are all well aware of the severe limitations on the funding of research today. On the other hand, I feel that one of the traps that we have fallen into, so far, is reliance on quick-look, undermanned and underfunded programs to investigate a tremendous quantity of often ambiguous data. I would discourage such programs as being diversionary, in regard to the overall scientific goal.

The goal of understanding anomalistic phenomena, if attained, may be of unprecedented importance to the human race. We must get a positive scientific program off the ground; a program that progresses according to the highest scientific standards, has specific objectives, is well funded, and long term.

Thank you.

# 7.

THE closing discussion that followed Dr. Baker's testimony reemphasized the reasons for the lack of UFO evidence produced by the various surveillance systems constantly in operation over our skies. As Dr. McDonald brings out, a constant question among laymen is: If UFO's exist, why aren't they tracked? Dr. Sagan's proposal that our surveillance radar may be throwing away much significant data that might reveal UFO evidence is interesting, because the system is equipped now to reject almost anything except those objects that are on a missile trajectory.

Congressman Roush started the informal summaries off:

We thought we would reserve the final few minutes for those of you who have made presentations to discuss among yourselves questions which may have been aroused by one of your colleagues' presentations today.

With that in mind, we are going to permit you to have a real free for all. Dr. Sagan.

Dr. SAGAN. I just wanted to underline one point that Dr. Baker made, Congressman Roush, in his detailed presentation of the various Air Force systems. I am afraid that the main point won't come across to a lay audience, and that is that with relatively little expenditure of funds, it would be possible to significantly improve the available information.

Apparently what is now happening is that the Air Force surveillance radar is throwing away the data that is of relevance for this inquiry. In other words, if it sees something that is not on a ballistic trajectory, or not in orbit, it ignores it, it throws it in the garbage.

Well, that garbage is just the area of our interest. So if some method could be devised by the Air Force to save the output that they are throwing away from these space surveillance radars, it might be the least expensive way to significantly improve our information about these phenomena.

Mr. ROUSH. Thank you.

Dr. BAKER. Let me just make a comment: That is quite true. At the present time our space surveillance sensors are about 200 percent overtasked. That means they could make about 50 percent of their time available to us. They task too many space objects, their capacity is much greater than the space objects that they are tasked to watch. The space population may grow to fill this void, but currently what Dr. Sagan says is true, we could as I indicated in conclusion (4) modify our current space surveillance system.

It is not an expensive thing to modify existing radars. The FPS-85 itself costs something like $100 million. The soft ware modification called for here I am sure would be much less.

Mr. ROUSH. Dr. Hynek.

Dr. HYNEK. I would just like to concur in what Dr. Sagan has said. I understand there are several hundred UCT's a month, uncorrelated targets, that because they don't—I understand—which since they do not follow ballistic trajectory, they are tossed out. It would not be expensive to introduce a sub-routine into the computer to take care of these things for a short while. I strongly second Dr. Sagan's and Dr. Baker's suggestions.

Mr. BOONE. Mr. Chairman.

Mr. ROUSH. Mr. Boone.

Mr. BOONE. I think the gentleman should advise you too, though, when you do that, you must make a trajectory determination on each target including aircraft which may put a terrific burden on the radar you are insisting on upgrading.

Dr. HYNEK. I will certainly grant that.

Dr. HARDER. I would only respond to Mr. Boone by suggesting you could reject all objects that were found, for instance, under 90,000 feet.

Dr. SAGAN. That is just what I was going to say. Certain velocity and altitude limitations.

Mr. BOONE. With that I agree. But I don't think we make many sightings at that altitude. We do have a problem here of what you want to look at. So in fact I think the thrust of Dr. Baker's argument here was that most of the Air Force equipment do not supply the material you would like to have.

So you are going to have to go to a much lower altitude, and you are going to have to check a much larger number of targets.

Dr. SAGAN. I may have misunderstood, but my understanding was, since all of these "uninteresting," trajectory objects are thrown away, we have no way of knowing at the present time whether there are or are not large numbers of interesting objects at altitudes above 90,000 feet.

Mr. BOONE. What this means is you check each one and determine its trajectory, and then throw it away, so it no longer becomes a simple task of saying "Oh, I only want to look at the unidentified ones." I have to check each one, and discard it.

Dr. SAGAN. Isn't that being done already?

Mr. BOONE. No, it doesn't do it below certain altitudes.

Dr. SAGAN. Right.

Mr. BOONE. All right. Certain targets are picked up at certain ranges, are they not?

Dr. SAGAN. Right. So therefore the suggestion is that within the altitude range, that is being used anyway by the surveillance radar——

Mr. BOONE. You complicate the procedure.

Dr. SAGAN. Slightly.

Mr. BOONE. The procedure is used but it involves the software again which is much more difficult to add to the systems than I believe is being presented. It can be done, there is no question it can be done.

Dr. HARDER. I would agree the amount of effort that goes into the relative softwares, although by no means a $100 million project, it is not a very simple project.

Mr. ROUSH. Dr. McDonald, do you have a comment?

Dr. McDONALD. Yes. I would underscore another one of the points, the general points that Dr. Baker made. I think it addresses itself to the question raised. Both scientists and members of the public are quite aware we have many monitoring radar systems, optical and so on.

This question is raised often, why aren't UFO's tracked? The point one is struck with in studying each of these systems in turn is the large degree of selectivity that is necessarily built into them. Good examples were cited by Dr. Baker.

It has to be kept well in mind that even systems like SAGE when they were developed necessarily had to have programed into them certain speed limits both lower and upper, certain safe requirements like if the target was on an outbound path it could be ignored. In almost every monitoring system you set up, whether for defense or scientific purposes, if you don't want to be snowed with data, you intentionally built selectivity in, and then you do not see what you are not looking for.

Consequently, this point is important, that despite our

many sensing and monitoring systems, the fact that they don't repeatedly turn up what appear to be similar to UFO's, whatever we define those to be, is not quite as conclusive as it might seem.

The second comment I would make concerns Dr. Baker's remark that we should move ahead to instrumental techniques and perhaps lessen attention on the older data.

I too agree that we have much need to replace what police officers and pilots saw with good hard instrumental data, the sooner the better, but there are many fields in which once you get instrumental data, say seismology, and begin to learn about the phenomenon you are studying, seismology, astronomy, meteorology, once you understand these things you do go back to exploit the knowledge that is implicit in older data. Seismologists do study old earthquake records to improve the seismicity data available. Ecologists do look at old shifts in plant and animal patterns. Astronomers do look at old eclipse information, because once you begin to understand a problem, you can then sort out much better the important material.

I would not want to see excluded entirely—in fact, I think it would be folly to exclude observations that go back 20 years, and a part of the problem we have not talked about today, still earlier observations.

Dr. BAKER. Yes, I concur in that.

My message there was that if we preoccupy ourselves with continually going over past history, it is going to be frustrating. I think we can always use past history in retrospect. In order to go back, as you say, to look at the data and to put it in the proper perspective, when we learn more about the phenomena. So I agree.

Mr. ROUSH. Is there any other aspect of previous presentations that any of you would like to question?

Dr. BAKER. I have a question of Dr. Harder about the Ubatuba magnesium.

Was this magnesium terrestrial? In other words, it is granted that Ubatubas couldn't produce it, but could the magnesium have been produced terrestrially, and if so, in what connection would we produce and employ such magnesium here on earth?

Dr. HARDER. Well, such pure magnesium is indeed produced terrestrially in connection with Grignard reagents, and produced by the Dow Chemical Co., where magnesium is produced in greater purity actually than this.

At the time in 1957, the Brazilians did not have a sample of magnesium from the U.S. Bureau of Standards that was as pure as this Ubatuba magnesium with which to compare it. I might enlarge upon the data which was produced, or which was gotten at the request of Dr. Craig, that of the impurities found by the Colorado group, the principal one was zinc strontium with barium being a runner-up. These are very curious kinds of alloys from any terrestrial point of view.

No detected aluminum, and only three parts per million copper, and those are the most likely alloying elements from the terrestrial point of view.

Dr. BAKER. Would you say that the sample was partially terrestrialized, and it might be the remnants of an ultrapure nonterrestrial alloy, or did it appear these particular impurities were in the sample from the beginning?

Dr. HARDER. This was done by a neutralization analysis on a very tiny slicer. It would be hard to say to what extent over the intervening 9 years there might be some territorialization, but certainly it would not have taken out aluminum or copper. It might have added zinc or barium, although that seems somewhat unlikely.

Dr. SAGAN. So some comparison analysis has been made for example of the magnesium flares. A magnesium flare has an abundance of impurities?

Dr. HARDER. It would hardly be 99.9 percent purity.

Dr SAGAN. That is what I meant.

Dr. HARDER. Yes, that is right.

Mr. Roush. Dr. McDonald.

Dr. McDONALD. Both Dr. Hall and Dr. Sagan remarked in different contexts on the intense emotional factors that predispose some people to certain systems of belief, and I would like to remark on that to be sure that some perspective is maintained on that part of the problem.

In the witnesses I have interviewed—I have intentionally stayed away from those who immediately show a very strong interest in a salvation theory, or something like that —so I have cut down my sample right at the start.

I would want to leave the point strongly emphasized that though there are a few people, and some of them rather visible and vocal, who are emotional about the problem and tie it to almost religious beliefs, the body of evidence that puzzles me, that bothers me, and I think demands much more scientific attention, comes from people who are really not at all emotional about it; they are puzzled by it, they are reliable, a typical cross-section of the populace. They have not built any wild theories on it.

In fact, let me mention one important sighting in New Guinea. I didn't interview the witness in New Guinea, but in Melbourne, Australia. An Anglican Missionary, Rev. William B. Gill, was teaching the school in New Guinea, and when he and some three dozen mission personnel saw an object hovering offshore with four figures visible on top of it, even this minister didn't begin to put any religious interpretation on it. He said this is what he saw, and he wrote very careful notes about it. It is that kind of evidence, and not evidence that comes from people with emotional factors predisposing them to system beliefs that impress me.

Mr. ROUSH. Let's have the psychologist speak here for just a moment.

Dr. HALL. Thank you.

I welcome that clarification.

The point I was making was not that the witnesses generally are emotional and precommitted to a position at all, but that the people who are interpreting the evidence after it has been gathered are usually precommitted beyond the point of rationality, and it is a very important distinction that you brought out.

The primary problem of witnesses, it seems to me, is this reluctance to report based apparently on a feeling that they will be ridiculed—that their evidence is not welcome—and I guess I can't resist telling the little story from the Wall Street Journal, quite recently, of a man who had five pet wallabys in Weschester County. A wallaby is a miniature kangaroo. These five wallabys escaped, and rather than upset people he didn't report this, he waited for people to tell him that they had seen them. And nothing happened for days and days.

Well, when they were finally relocated and caught then lots of people started admitting, yes, they had seen these wallabys, but after all, if you see a tiny kangaroo loping across the road in New Rochelle, you are reticent to report it.

Mr. ROUSH. Dr. Hynek again.

Dr. HYNEK. I think that is a most interesting point that ties in. I think sometimes we don't ask ourselves really very fundamental questions, and that is, how is it that these reports exist in the first place?

It is not just because they are strange, because we don't have reports of Christmas trees flying upside down, or elephants doing strange things in the sky; the reports are strange, but they do have a certain pattern.

Now, I have often asked myself, well, why do the reports exist in the first place? And how many are reported?

Whenever I give a presentation to some group I frequently will ask them, well, how many of you have seen something in the skies you couldn't explain; that is a UFO, or some friend whose veracity you can vouch for?

I have been surprised to find that 10 to 15 percent, albeit it is a specialized audience, they are there already because they are interested, hence there is a selection factor, but nonetheless I am quite surprised that many respond.

Then I ask the second one, Did you ever report it to the Air Force? And maybe one or two will say that they have.

Now, why, then, should people make reports anyway, since they face such great ridicule? They do it for two reasons, those that I have talked to: One, is out of a sense of civic duty. Time and again I will get a letter saying, I haven't said this to anybody, but I feel it is my duty as a citizen to report this. And many letters come to me. In fact, even saying, please do not report this to the Air Force.

The second reason is that their curiosity finally bugs them. They have been thinking about it and they want to know what it was they saw, and many letters I get will end in a rather plaintive note, can you possibly tell me, or can you tell me whether it is possible what I saw?

Those two reasons are the "springs" of why the report is made in the first place. I don't know how much store can be put in the Gallup poll, but I understand when, about 2 years ago a poll was made on this subject, there was something like—the poll reported 5 million people, 5 million Americans had seen something in the skies they could not explain. Over the past 20 years the Air Force has had some 12,000 reports. Therefore, one can logically ask, who is holding out on the other 4,988,000 reports?

I think there may be quite a reservoir of reports that simply have not come out into the open because of this natural reluctance of people to speak out.

Mr. ROUSH. Dr. Hynek, your experience has been similar to mine, although much more extensive. In the 10 years I have served on this committee I have had occasion to ask various witnesses their beliefs as far as UFO's are concerned. They have included Air Force generals and Army generals, and usually they display a great interest. Sometimes they will say, I don't believe, but my wife does; some will say.

As a result of my experience on this committee I have been privileged to visit the tracking stations which NASA has throughout the world. Each place I have visited I have asked the question, "Have you tracked any unidentified flying objects?"

Well, it is obvious they apparently don't have the ability to track, but the response was "No," everywhere except in South Africa. Then they said, "Anything we track, which we do not understand, we turn over to the Department of Defense," inferring there were some things they did not understand.

The same is true with those places in the world where there is a Baker-Nunn camera. I asked the same question of them. For the most part there was a boundless curiosity, but a negative response.

Dr. HYNEK. I might respond to that, of course, in talking to them, you have represented officialdom, and they may themselves be a little afraid to say anything to a Congressman that might get them into trouble.

But I get reports subrosa that are to the effect that people, trackers, and so forth, have seen things, but they would not dare think of reporting it.

Now, that is hearsay. I am sorry it is not hearsay; it has happened to me.

But it is not what I would call "solid evidence."

Mr. ROUSH. Just one other comment. I serve on the board of trustees of a college back in Indiana. In the course of a year they had numerous lectures by outstanding people in their lecture series, quite outstanding people on various subjects, but they scheduled one lecture given by a student at the college on unidentified flying objects. Needless to say, he had the best attendance of the entire series.

Dr. Harder.

Dr. HARDER. Following on something that Dr. Hynek said about the small percentage of actual sightings that are reported, this would suggest that the two instances that I brought out, which to my knowledge are the only extant pieces of what you might call scientific information—information containing information of a scientific nature, might well be multiplied by a factor of 10, if it were not for this ridicule bit, and furthermore, if it were not the subject of ridicule, many people would perhaps take greater care in the observations that they do make, and perhaps come up with similar kinds of anecdotal nature of somewhat more importance than just flashing lights.

For instance, the plane of polarization or—well, many kinds of observations came to us. We would have even at this point far more anecdotal information of a scientific nature and of scientific importance than we now have.

Mr. ROUSH. I think those of you who have sat on this panel today have made perhaps a greater contribution than you realize in adding some respectability to the interest the American people have in this phenomena [sic]. Perhaps we can, by further activity on the part of this committee, and you on your part, and by the public reading what you have said today, cause people to be more responsive and to report what they see. Perhaps we can thereby give an air of respectability to these sightings which will permit people to go ahead without being embarrassed or ashamed of reporting what they have seen.

Does anyone else have anything here?

Mr. FULTON. Mr. Chairman, sightings of UFO's in western Pennsylvania have now increased to the point where interested citizens have established a UFO Research Institute with a 24-hour answering service, to investigate reports and sightings.

In my congressional district, there is the Westinghouse astronuclear plant, whose fine work is well known to the members of our committee. As I have been asked by Mr. Stanton T. Friedman, a nuclear physicist at Westinghouse who makes a hobby of investigating UFO sightings and publicly speaking on the subject, it is a pleasure to insert a statement by Mr. Friedman, "Flying Saucers Are Real" into the record at this point. He is one of the few observers with the candor to conclude and so state that "the earth is being visited by intelligently controlled vehicles" from outer space.

Mr. ROUSH. Dr. Baker, and Dr. Hall, Dr. McDonald, Dr. Harder, Dr. Hynek, and Dr. Sagan, I believe that you people have made a real contribution here, and I think the time will come when certain people will look back and read what has been done here today and realize that we have pioneered in a field insofar as the Congress of the United States is concerned. They will be very mindful that something worthwhile was done here today.

As a personal note, I would like to say this has been one of the most unusual and most interesting days I have spent since I have been in the Congress of the United States.

Thank you.

I thank each of you.

# 8.

THE spoken testimony added up to a powerful and cogent dissent to the conclusion that Dr. Condon was later to draw from the research work of his Colorado staff. But it is interesting to note that the positions of the scientists appearing before Congress were not half so much at odds with the material in the Condon Report as they were with Condon's *personal* conclusion and interpretation.

Certainly the group of scientists at the hearing command as much respect as the Colorado study staff, yet the impact of the press releases about the latter study dwarfed the efforts of these men to make their story known.

Further, the written reports filed by those scientists who could not appear at the hearings revealed the urgent need for continuing UFO study—with the lone exception of Dr. Menzel, who has been espousing the negative cause for many years. His referral to himself as "the leading exponent of opposing views" characterizes both his position and his self-appraisal with great economy of phrase.

Menzel's\* attempt to equate *all* UFO sightings with natural phenomena or mistaken identity shows so many weaknesses in the face of the documented evidence that it seems strange that he continues to hold onto this point of view so stubbornly. He agrees that the concept of manned spaceships is not an absolute impossibility. He agrees that intel-

\* See Appendix I.

ligent life, perhaps more intelligent than ours, may exist in "the vast reaches of outer space," as he puts it. He admits that there might be as many as a million possible planets where intelligent life could exist.

Menzel further admits that the Air Force has made many mistakes, that they never have had enough scientists assigned to the UFO project, that they have failed to follow up certain sightings of special importance, that their questionnaire for UFO investigations is amateurish—"almost cleverly designed in certain cases, to get the wrong answer and lose track of the facts."

He further admits that many highly reliable people have reported seeing objects moving at fantastic speeds and "apparently taking evasive action in a manner impossible for known terrestrial craft." He concedes that by 1952 a "sizable" number in the Air Force had come to the conclusion that the only explanation for UFOs was that they were extraterrestrial vehicles.

He then goes on to conclude that intelligent people have been tricked by such things as "power lines, insulators, television antennas . . . even apartment windows." He does not go on to conclude how hundreds of thousands—possibly millions—of people, many of them experts, can *all* be fooled, *all* the time, especially with multiple witnesses, corroborative radar data, accompanying photos, electromagnetic effects, ground markings, or strange effects on animals. None of this evidence seems to get through to Dr. Menzel. He seems to ignore the impact of low-altitude, close-range sightings by responsible people over a long period of time.

His written statement to the Congressional hearing mounts in growing nonscientific passion, reaching a crescendo with the sentence: "It is time that we put an end to chasing ghosts, hobgoblins, visions, and hallucinations."

We are thus left with the disquieting thought that up to five million people, most of whom are granted by Menzel and Condon to be sane and responsible, are suffering from the above "ghosts, hobgoblins, visions, and hallucinations."

Fortunately, another written statement filed with the House Committee on Science and Astronautics by Dr. Garry C. Henderson, senior research scientist for General Dynamics, takes a good stiff look at Dr. Menzel's nightmarish concept. As Project Leader of the lunar surface gravimeter surveying system for his company, Dr. Henderson is not without sophistication on space projects. He writes:

Most thoughtful persons will dismiss the theatrical claims of trips on "saucers" . . . however, some very plausible reports from highly trained, capable, and reliable individuals cannot be so readily discarded by anyone willing to admit that there are still a few things we do not understand.

*God help us if our military and commercial pilots and radar facilities so commonly mistake temperature inversions, balloons, atmospheric disturbances, the planet Venus, etc. for maneuvering vehicles. Have you ever tried to convince two veteran pilots that the object they reported sighting on a clear day with CAVU conditions, free of traffic lanes, showing on their radar screen, exhibiting high maneuverability, in close proximity, etc., is meteoric debris? If so, then the wrong people are being examined.* *

Dr. Leo Sprinkle, the psychologist from the University of Wyoming, echoes a similar thought in the statement he filed with the committee, which is also in sharp contrast to Dr. Menzel's theories:

I have read thousands of [UFO] reports and I have talked with hundreds of persons about their UFO observations; either I must accept the view that thousands of people have observed physical phenomena, or I must accept the view that thousands of

* Italics mine.

persons have the ability to project mental images in such a manner that other persons can observe, photograph, and obtain physical evidence of those mental images.

In the written statement filed by Stanton T. Friedman,* another reaction to Dr. Menzel's thinking is recorded. Mr. Friedman, who holds his master's degree in science from the University of Chicago, is a Fellow Scientist with the Westinghouse Astronuclear Laboratory, working on the nuclear rocket program. Regarding the outlook of not only Menzel, but also Marcowitz (a scientist protesting that interstellar distances are too great for space travel) and Klass (the plasma and ball-lightning theorist), he writes:

The paper by Marcowitz and the books by Menzel and Klass will undoubtedly be read by scientists in the 21st century as "classics" illustrating a non-scientific approach to UFOs by people who, for whatever reason, would not examine the data relevant to UFOs or advanced technology. Marcowitz was totally wrong about fission and fusion propulsion systems, didn't even consider electromagnetic propulsion, and was obviously unaware of current technology. . . . McDonald has discussed Menzel's approach in detail. . . . I agree with Klass in only one item: many people have observed glowing plasmas; but I believe they were adjacent to vehicles rather than ball lightning or corona discharge. He didn't even consider this possibility despite all his talk about plasmas and despite the enormous amount of plasma-vehicle data which is available. In summary, I feel that these three gentlemen have made strong attempts to make the data fit their hypotheses rather than trying to do the much more difficult job of creating hypotheses which fit the data.

Dr. Richard N. Shepard, formerly professor and a director of the psychological laboratories at Harvard and now professor of psychology at Stanford University, also sub-

* See Appendix.

mitted a scholarly and detailed report to the committee. He has published some thirty technical and scientific papers on human perception. In opposition to Menzel's point of view, he feels that the human observer has consistently been sold short. Noting that the study of UFO phenomena is more amenable to the methods of the psychologist than to those of the physical scientist, he writes:

I do not mean to suggest by this that most reports of UFOs can probably be shown to arise from purely psychological aberrations such as illusions, hallucinations, delusions, and the like. On the contrary, a careful examination of most of the best-documented cases has convinced me—as at least one psychologist who has studied rather extensively into the fields of normal and psychopathological perception—that very few such cases can be explained along these lines. Indeed, I have the impression that the claims that the UFOs reported even by seemingly responsible citizens represent lapses of a basically psychopathological character have generally come from people who have neglected to study closely either into the literature on psychopathology, or into that on UFOs, or—in many cases, I fear—both.

In other words, Menzel's theories do not seem to stand up under hard scrutiny from this specialist's point of view, just as they have been contested by nearly every scientist contributing to the symposium.

When Dr. Menzel asks the hypothetical question in his statement: "Why should one [UFO] not have landed and shown himself to the President of the United States, to a member of the National Academy of Sciences, or at least to some member of Congress?" he is echoing a question that many of us ask. It is of course purely a speculative one, just as any answer must be speculative in reply. The next contributor to the symposium who filed a written appearance attempts to answer this, as well as any hypothetical question of this sort can be answered. He is Dr. Frank Salisbury, head of the Plant Science Department of Utah State University, with a specialty in space biology. He submitted for his contribution an article he wrote for *Bio-Science:*

Another argument against the spaceship idea concerns the lack of formal contact with the UFO occupants. Since visiting spaceships ought to be piloted by some sort of intelligent beings, wouldn't it be reasonable to expect that they would desire contact with other intelligent beings, namely us? Or why hasn't a flying saucer landed on the United Nations building to establish formal diplomatic relations?

This argument assumes that we can understand the motives of an extraterrestrial being. Of course we cannot. How could we know the minds of such beings? To inductively extrapolate from our own current sociological approaches to those of other intelligent entities would be to commit the logical sin of extrapolation in a most flagrant manner. It is easy to imagine several reasons why the extraterrestrials might not want to contact us. Did they plant us here as a colony many thousands of years ago and are carefully observing our evolutionary development? Do they envy us for our natural resources and want to conquer us, although present logistic problems make such an effort impossible? Are they waiting for us to straighten out our wars and race problems? Are they simply uninterested in us as contemporaries, preferring to observe us as specimens? Entomologists study the honeybees very carefully, but make no contact with the queen!

Imagine the Aborigines of Central Australia, who are still in the Stone Age, and who have not even developed the bow and arrow. They have had no contact at all with modern civilization. What happens when a jet plane flies overhead and one of them observes it? When he tells of the huge, shiny bird that didn't flap its wings, and no feet, made an ear-splitting roar, and even had smoke coming out of its tail, surely his fellows assume that he is crazy. Or if the phenomenon becomes so common that it must be accepted as real, they could hardly be expected to deduce from it the conditions of our modern civilization, let alone our motives. "Why," they might ask, "don't the intelligent beings who guide this mighty bird land, and trade bone nosepieces with us?" Actually, many of the Aborigines, even those who have come in contact with civilized men, still interpret the airplane in a religious context, as witness the establishment of the cargo cults among these peoples.

Other scientists who disagree most heartily with Menzel's negative theories point out that it is most homocentric for us to assume that an advanced civilization would have a special and intense interest in the earth when there are so many millions of other possibly civilized planets scattered throughout the universe. Still others have reported that recommendations for our own future astronauts include suggestions that no contact should be made until we have thoroughly surveyed a planet with possible life on it, taking care not to arouse possible population. Another hypothetical answer to this hypothetical question is that if there is an extremely long life span in another advanced civilization, its exploration of our planet over a period of twenty years might be relatively equivalent to only a few of our hours or minutes, in which case they might plan to make contact at a later time. But all of this is so speculative that it doesn't bear directly on the reasonably hardcore evidence of the better cases.

The six scientists whose testimony has been discussed went into much more detail and prescribed much more action than is recorded here. With the exception of Menzel, all were convinced that only long and continuing study could solve this mystery, and that scientific paydirt was almost certain to come out of the investigation.

But what are the conclusions to be drawn from the House UFO hearings, and why are they important?

They are important first because the testimony at these

hearings is at direct odds with the Condon study, which had a fully documented shadow of prejudice over it from its very inception.

Beyond that, eleven out of twelve sober and articulate scientists have, in these hearings, stated clearly that the UFO problem not only is unsolved, but urgently needs to be solved for a variety of reasons.

It has been demonstrated that the work of Dr. Condon's own staff is, in the most crucial points, directly at odds with his personal conclusions. His reasons for choosing to ignore these data can only be speculated upon. The failure of the National Academy of Sciences to question his conclusions is even more mystifying.

But this is not at all unusual throughout history. Every scientist worth his salt faced incredible prejudice and even persecution from the most sanctified institutions of his day. Newton, Galileo, Einstein, Pasteur, Freud, and dozens of others were faced with almost vicious opposition in their attempts to establish what they rationally were convinced to be the truth. They did not ask for approval; they asked for reason. They did not ask for bias; they asked for understanding. They did not ask for applause; they asked for objectivity—even in the face of data that were at odds with contemporary scientific understanding.

Any "oppositionist," if honest, reasonable, gentle, tolerant, and inquiring, does not want a slavish accolade for his discernment of a pattern that goes against accepted theory and practice. What applies to a good scientist also applies to a good journalist, and I emphasize the importance of the word "good," banal as it has become.

A good journalist, when he goes out on a story, must keep with him an attitude of toughness. He knows that if he becomes what is known in the vernacular as a sucker, he is in deep trouble. Like anyone else, he does not want to be taken in by a fairy tale, for he will be ruined if he does. He may take everything else with a sense of humor, but not his work. The same is true with the scientist. He must not, at the risk of professional suicide, let himself be hoodwinked by unsubstantiated data.

As a journalist I finally reached the point in my careful research at Exeter where I realized that a so-called single UFO report turned out to be more than sixty such incidents. Then I was willing to stick my neck out, I did so only because I could do nothing else in the face of the material that was being unearthed.

This material was exotic, strange, mystifying, incredible, startling, alarming. To accept it as evidence was dangerous. To reject it was literally wrong. The only thing I could do was to be as sure of my ground as I could possibly be, and let it go at that. There were moments when I wanted to forget the whole thing. I kept asking myself how was I going to explain my conclusion to friends of mine who were, for the most part, even more cynical than I was? I kept worrying about my reputation. Was I unwittingly to become one of those who calls himself a "UFO expert"? This was the last thing in the world I wanted to be, or still want to be. The point is that I cannot sit back and watch others, including scientists, distort and challenge my honest observations without their doing as much legwork as I did.

No one has ever successfully challenged the hard-core material in either *Incident at Exeter* or *The Interrupted Journey* from the point of view of honest and direct reporting. I would be surprised if they could successfully do so, because I was more cautious than any critic could be in accepting the testimony I found myself suddenly facing. I had written very critical books about the stock market and heavy industry, books so critical that I could have been sued heavily if I had been wrong. Naturally, I checked and re-checked every fact I wrote—and carried this same careful approach into the subject of UFOs.

But think how much more vulnerable the scientists who spoke out so directly at these Congressional hearings before the Committee on Science and Astronautics are. As a journalist, I could be much more relaxed and loose about my observations than they were (although I always hoped that I was most careful about this). But at this hearing on July 29, 1968, solid, careful, distinguished scientists reached a conclusion in direct opposition to that of Dr. Condon. In doing so they have stuck their necks out far more than I have. But their argument and persuasion contain the ring of truth, not prejudice; the caution of the dissenter, not the arrogance of the officially endowed; the perception of the curious, not the dogma of the biased. As such, their words must stand side by side with the Condon Committee Report in equal strength. The public will eventually decide which will stand up in the perspective of history.

# Appendix I

IN preparing his report, Dr. Condon did not make a single field investigation, as a NICAP bulletin points out. He failed to interview a single pilot, astronomer, aerospace engineer, control tower operator or any other competent witness that NICAP offered as evidence. The Condon Report still leaves the UFO question wide open, and in fact adds some convincing evidence, in spite of Dr. Condon's personal stance.

The attitude of Dr. Condon is most clearly paralleled by the report submitted to the House Committee on Science and Astronautics by Dr. Donald H. Menzel, which is reprinted here in full as an example of how a trained scientist with a good analytical mind can shut his eyes to facts that are so thoroughly documented that the only alternative conclusion is that thousands of expert or competent reports are the result of either insanity or gross incompetence.

Dr. Menzel begins his attack against the scientists who testified at these Congressional hearings—many of whom are equally competent to express their opinions technically—by calling UFOs a modern myth. At the same time, strangely enough, he makes several admissions:

—He concedes that the concept of manned spaceships from extraterrestrial sources is not an impossibility.
—He concedes that it is very possible that intelligent life—even more intelligent than we—may exist in outer space.
—He concedes that there might be, as an educated guess, as high as a million habitable planets in our own Milky Way.
—He concedes that the Air Force has made its mistakes, that

they failed to follow up on several important sightings, that their questionnaire is amateurish.

—He concedes that *highly reliable* persons have reported UFOs moving at incredible speeds and in such a way as to be impossible for terrestrial craft.

—He concedes that by 1952 *a sizable number of Air Force personnel* had concluded that extraterrestrial vehicles were the *only possible explanation* for the phenomenon.

With all these concessions, it would seem strange that he failed to consider the UFO subject as one that deserved extremely careful attention, instead of the haphazard treatment given to it by the Condon Committee.

Dr. Menzel then goes on to establish his position: That natural explanations exist for the unexplained sightings.

To reach this conclusion, Dr. Menzel points out the frailties of human observation, *as if nearly every competent witness to a sighting didn't have the brains to take these frailties into account before filing a report.*

Menzel is not the only one who seeks to find a natural explanation before accepting a sighting as valid, yet he writes in just such a way. Witnesses I have interviewed personally nearly always tell me the lengths they went to to explain their sightings before they reluctantly had to conclude that there *was* no natural explanation. Menzel constantly fails to take into account that scientists, pilots, radar men, and other competent witnesses questioned and examined their own observations. The scientists who testified at the hearing in exact opposition to Menzel's views had *already allowed for* the anomalies that Menzel takes so many pains to point out. The very definition of a "competent" witness would include the capacity for rationally questioning tricks that the eyes play on a person, hoaxes, misidentifications, and all the other phenomena that Menzel dwells on.

Nobody would argue against Menzel that a great percentage of the sightings can be explained in this way. It is the residual cases that count. When so many observers go to such great length to rule out the very points that Menzel rests his case on, it can only be considered a form of arrogance to question them—especially when many carry just as high and distinguished technical qualifications as Menzel.

Menzel goes on to talk about the Robertson Panel and its CIA investigation of the subject. He seems to hold a great deal of faith in this investigation. I talked to one member of the Robertson Panel, a very distinguished scientist, who told me that the panel met for a very short time, did no direct investigation itself, superficially screened a lot of data prepared by the Air Force, and reached its negative conclusion on the most shallow and superficial glance at the material. With such a complex subject, it would seem impossible for any panel to reach an intelligent conclusion on this basis. It is almost unimaginable that it would do so. Yet this is the type of conclusion that Dr. Menzel puts so much faith in.

Menzel's entire paper submitted to the Congressional committee does little more than dwell on the weak and insubstantial cases, and ignores the critical and baffling cases. He goes on ad nauseam about "after images," which is a phenomenon known to every high-school graduate and easily ruled out by any intelligent person. He talks about hoaxes as if he were the only one to consider this possibility as one of the first things to rule out. He talks about the "vast field of atmospheric physics," which is the life work of Dr. James McDonald, whose point of view is diametrically opposed to that of Dr. Menzel.

Most revealing is Dr. Menzel's statement, "I know of no reliable case of simultaneous visual and radar sightings."

In the light of this statement, perhaps Dr. Menzel could increase his own knowledge by first reading Dr. Condon's own case histories as mentioned in the foreword of this book, and then consulting both NICAP and some of the other scientists at this Congressional hearing who have devoted a great deal of time and serious energy to this most mystifying subject.

## PREPARED STATEMENT BY DONALD H. MENZEL
### UFO: FACT OR FICTION?

Flying saucers or UFO's have been with us for a long time. June 24, 1968 marked the 21st anniversary of the sighting of nine bright discs moving rapidly along the hogback of Mount Rainier. However, similar sightings go far back in history, where they have assumed various forms for different people. Old records refer to them as fiery dragons, fiery chariots, wills-o'-the-wisp, jack-o'-lanterns, *ignis fatuus,* firedrakes, fox-fire, and even the devil himself.

And now a new legend—a modern myth—has arisen to explain a new rash of mysterious sightings. Certain UFO buffs argue that the peculiar properties and maneuvers of these apparitions, as reported by reliable people of all kinds, are so remarkable that only one explanation for them is possible. They must be vehicles from outer space, manned by beings far more intelligent than we, because the operators have clearly built vehicles with capabilities far beyond anything we can conceive of.

On the face of it, this reasoning sounds much like that of Sherlock Holmes, who said on several occasions: "It is an old maxim of mine that when you have excluded the impossible, whatever remains, however improbable, must be the truth!"

I am willing to go along with this formula, but only after we have followed Holmes and excluded every possibility but that of manned UFO's. And we must also show that no further possible solutions exist.

The believers are too eager to reach a decision. The method is simple. They try to find someone, whom they can establish as an authority, who will support their views. They then quote and often misquote various authorities or one another until they believe what they are saying. Having no real logic on their side, they resort to innuendo as a weapon and try to discredit those who fail to support their view. The UFO magazines refer to me as the arch-demon of saucerdom!

I concede that the concept of manned spaceships is not an absolute impossibility. Neither are the concepts of ghosts, spirits, witches, fairies, elves, hobgoblins, or the devil. The only trouble with this last list is the fact that they are out of date. We live in the age of space. Is it not natural that beings from outer space should exhibit an interest in us? But, when we consider that these beings—if indeed they are beings—have been bugging us for centuries, why should one not have landed and shown himself to the President of the United States, to a member of the National Academy of Sciences, or at least to some member of Congress?

Please don't misunderstand me. I think it is very possible that intelligent life—perhaps more intelligent than we—may exist somewhere in the vast reaches of outer space. But it is the very vastness of this space that complicates the problem. The distances are almost inconceivable. The time required to reach the earth—even at speeds comparable with that of light—range in hundreds if not thousands of years for our near neighbors. And it takes light some billions of years to reach us from the most distant galaxies, times comparable with that for the entire life history of our solar system. The number of habitable planets in the universe is anybody's guess. Any figures you may have heard, including mine, are just guesses. I have guessed that our own Milky Way may contain as many as a million such planets. That sounds like a lot, but the chances are the nearest such inhabited planet would be so distant that if we send out a message to it today we should have to wait some 2000 years for a reply. Alas, the evidence is poor for intelligent life in our solar system, though I do expect some lower forms of life to exist on Mars.

With respect to UFO's my position is simply this. That natural explanations exist for the unexplained sightings. The Air Force has given me full access to their files. There is no vast conspiracy of either the Air Force or CIA to conceal the facts from the public, as some groups have charged. The basic reason for continued reporting of UFO's lies in the possibility—just the possibility mind you—that some of them may derive from experimentation or secret development of a hostile power. And I don't mean hostile beings from outer space!

The Air Force has made its mistakes. They never have had enough scientists in the project. They have failed to follow up certain sightings of special importance. Their questionnaire is amateurish, almost cleverly designed in certain cases to get the wrong answer and lose track of the facts. The Air Force is aware of my criticism and, on a voluntary basis, I have helped them improve the questionnaire. It was not an easy job. Especially when the Air Force rejected some vital questions as "an invasion of the privacy of the individual."

From 1947 until 1954 a bewildered group of Air Force personnel tried honestly and sincerely to resolve the UFO problem. Many highly reliable persons had reported seeing "objects" moving at fantastic speeds, and apparently taking evasive action in a manner impossible for known terrestrial craft. By 1952 a sizable number of those in the Air Force group had concluded that extraterrestrial vehicles were the only explanation. Some of this unrest leaked out. Popular writers exploited these ideas and soon various UFO clubs came into existence. In 1953, a committee of scientists, headed by the late H. P. Robertson of California Institute of Technology met at CIA to consider a number of the Air Force's most convincing cases. They immediately solved many of them. Others could not be solved because of poor or insufficient data. They concluded that all cases had a natural solution. There was no evidence to support the idea that UFO's are vehicles from another world.

Nevertheless, the UFO buffs believe, almost as an article of faith, that "trained observers," such as military or airline pilots, could not possibly mistake a meteor, a planet, a star, a sundog, or a mirage for a UFO. This viewpoint is absolutely nonsense and the Air Force files bear witness to its falsity! They contain thousands of solved cases—sightings by "reliable individuals" like the pilots: But such persons have made huge errors in identification.

A huge meteor flashes in the sky! The co-pilot thinks it is going to strike the plane and takes evasive action. The pilot disagrees and he is right. The UFO proves to be a fireball or meteor a hundred miles away! Such occurrences are frequent, not rare. They have been increased with the growing number of re-entries and spectacular decay of satellite debris from the space operations of the U.S.A. and the U.S.S.R.

Distances overhead are uncommonly hard to estimate—either on the ground or in the air. A bird's feather, shining brightly in the sun and floating a mere 20 feet overhead may seem to be a distant object moving at very high speed. Conversely, a pilot may think that a bright object on the horizon, in reality a star or planet, lies just beyond his wing tip. Sometimes, a layer of warm air, sandwiched between 2 layers of cold air, can act as a lens, projecting a pulsing, spinning, vividly colored, saucer-like image of a planet. Pilots, thinking they were dealing with a nearby flying object, have often tried to intercept the image, which evades all attempts to cut it off. The distance may seem to change rapidly, as the star fades or increases in brightness. Actual "dog fights" have been recorded between a confused military pilot and a planet. I myself have observed this phenomenon of star mirage. It is both realistic and frightening.

Such observations fortified the UFO legend—that these objects "maneuver as if under intelligent control." But the pilots failed to realize that the "intelligent control" came from within themselves. And I think that Air Force personnel of Project Blue Book still do not appreciate this important UFO phenomenon.

Mirages are not the only apparitions that appear to maneuver. I think I was the first person to point out that a special kind of reflection of the sun (or moon), sometimes called a sun dog (or moon dog), also can perform evasive action. Layers of ice crystals are necessary, like those found in cirrus clouds. An aviator flying through cirrus sometimes sees a peculiar metallic appearing reflection, a reflection of the sun or moon. He may elect to chase it. The apparition will recede if approached, or approach if the pilot reverses his course. The object seems to execute *evasive action!* As the pilot runs out of ice crystals, the UFO will seem to put on a burst of speed and disappear into the distance.

But such behavior does not imply, as the UFO addicts argue, the presence of an intelligence pilot to guide it. No! It's like chasing a rainbow, which recedes as you approach it or advances as you move away.

As we look over the Air Force files, we find that some 90 per cent of the solved cases result from the presence of material objects in the atmosphere. I list some of these objects. Reflections from airplanes, banking in the sun, simulate saucers. Momentarily, a bright reflection appears and then vanishes. The plane is invisible in the distant haze. An imaginative person concludes that an interplanetary vehicle has come in fast, reversed course, and rapidly receded into the distance. Often the observers say "It couldn't have been a plane," because "no noise was heard" or because "it moved too swiftly." And yet careful study proves beyond doubt that the object was indeed an aircraft. The brilliant landing lights of a plane can almost dazzle a person on the ground. Sometimes such lights may appear to be very close—only a few hundred feet away.

You'd be surprised at the variety of mundane objects that people have reported as UFO's. Balloons, child's balloons, weather balloons lighted or unlighted, and especially those enormous plastic balloons as large as a ten-story building, which carry scientific instruments to altitudes of 100,000 feet! Reflecting full sunlight while the earth below lies in dim twilight, these balloons shine more brilliantly than Venus! Advertising planes or illuminated blimps frequently become UFO's.

Birds, by day or night, often reflect light from their shiny backs. Windblown kites, hats, paper, plastic sacks, feathers, spiderwebs, seed pods, dust devils have all contributed to their share of UFO sightings. Insects single or in swarms. Saucer-shaped clouds, reflections of searchlights on clouds! Special space experiments, such as rocket-launched sodium vapor releases or balloons from Wallop's Island have also produced spectacular apparitions! Ball lightning and the Aurora Borealis occasionally contribute.

Reflections from power lines, insulators, television antennas, radars, radio telescopes, even apartment windows! These, too, have produced realistic UFO's.

I could add to this list almost indefinitely. But the chief point I want to make is that simple phenomena like the above have tricked intelligent people into reporting a UFO.

But there are a few other phenomena that can produce UFO's of a type that, as far as I know, the Air Force still does not recognize.

I quote from an article on "Vision" in Volume 14 of the McGraw-Hill Encyclopedia of Science and Technology. ". . . any observant person can detect swirling clouds or spots of 'light' in total darkness or while looking at a homogeneous field such as a bright blue sky." If you want to see flying saucers just look up. If you don't see them, you probably are not "observant."

I see them most clearly in a dark room or on a moonless night with the sky even darker with heavy clouds. I find stars somewhat distracting. Just lie down on your back, open your eyes and see the saucers spin. The show is free. You will almost surely see bright, irregular patches of light form. Most of them seem grey green, but I occasionally see silver or gold and occasionally red. I can imagine windows in some of them. As you move your eyes they will cavort over the sky. To speed up the action just rub your eyes like a person coming out of a sleep. Occasionally the whole field becomes large and luminous. Now, I ask you. How can you be sure that the UFO reported by an airline pilot is not one of these spurious images? And even if an alerted co-pilot confirms it, he might also be responding to a similar effect in his own eyes!

The chemistry and physiology of the human eyes are certainly responsible for many UFO sightings. The eye responds in different ways to different kinds of stimuli. A sudden burst of bright light, like that from a flash bulb, for example, exerts an enduring effect on the eye. The light from the flash produces an immediate change in the so-called visual purple of the retina. In a sense the retinal spot on which the image fell becomes fatigued. For some minutes after the flash you will be able to see a bright, usually greenish, floating spot, which could be mistaken for a UFO by someone unfamiliar with the problem.

Let me take an actual case, which is typical of a large number actually in the files of Project Blue Book. A child, going to the bathroom turns on a bright light and accidentally awakens one of his parents who is blinded by the sudden illumination. The light goes off and the parent gets up to investigate and just happens to glance out of the window. He is startled to see a peculiar spot of light floating over the trees and making irregular, jerky motions. He watches the UFO for a minute or two until it finally disappears.

He cannot be blamed for failing to realize that the erratic and often rapid movements of his UFO are those of the after-image, drifting with the similar movements of his own eye. The UFO appears in the direction he happens to be looking. That is all. And yet he may describe it graphically as a luminous object "cavorting around in the sky."

Many such stimuli are possible by day or night. Some time ago I was driving directly toward the setting sun. When I came to a stop-light and looked out the side window of the car, I was startled to see a large, black object shaped something like a dirigible, surrounded by dozens of small black balloons. I suddenly realized that they were after-images of the sun. The big one was where I had been looking most fixedly. The spots were images where my eye had wandered. A UFO buff could have sworn that he was seeing a "mother ship" and a swarm of UFO's in rapid flight.

I once had another similar experience. I suddenly glanced up and was surprised to see a whole flotilla of UFO's flying in formation across the blue sky. They looked like after-images, but I hadn't been conscious of the visual stimulus responsible. I quickly retraced my steps and found it: sunlight reflected from the shiny surface of the fender of a parked car.

I am sure that many UFO's still unknowns, belong to this class. Look fixedly at the full moon for at least 30 seconds and then turn away. A greenish balloon will swim over your head and perform maneuvers startling or impossible for any real object. I've been able to attain the same effect with the planet Venus, when near maximum brilliance. Yet most observers will swear that such UFO's are true objects. And the Air Force questionnaire, failing to recognize even the existence of this kind of UFO, contains not a single question that would help them to identify it. In fact the words signifying UFO, unidentified flying object, show the state of mind of the Air Force personnel who invented this abbreviation. What I am saying is that the UFO's are not unidentifiable, they are often not flying, and many are not even objects. It is this point of view—to regard the apparitions as actual solid objects—that has retarded the solution so long.

After-images possess still other complicated characteristics. A colored light tends to produce an after-image with complementary color. A green flash will cause a red after-image and vice versa. Color-blind persons and persons with defective vision will often experience effects different from those of people with normal eyesight.

Another optical phenomenon that can produce an illusion of flying objects lies within the eye itself. Again, look at some uniformly bright surface—sky or ceiling. Relax your eyes. By that I mean focus your eyes on infinity. The chances are that you will see an array of dark spots. These specks, which may seem to be near like a swarm of gnats or as ill-defined objects at a distance, are either on or in your eye. They may be dust floating on the lens, minute imperfections in the cornea, or possible blood cells on the retina. These, too, can simulate evasive and erratic movement.

The eyeball jumps a little every time you blink. Walking transmits vibrations to the eye at every step. Many individuals think they see stars, planets, or satellites oscillating when the movement is actually that of the eye itself. Here is an example.

On our return across Minnesota we had an experience which I have always remembered as illustrative of the fallacy of all human testimony about ghosts, rappings, and other phenomena of that character. We spent two nights and a day at Fort Snelling. Some of the officers were greatly surprised by a celestial phenomenon of a very extraordinary character which had been observed for several nights past. A star had been seen, night after night, rising in the east as usual, and starting on its course toward the south. But instead of continuing that course across the meridian, as stars invariably had done from the remotest antiquity, it took a turn toward the north, sunk toward the horizon, and finally set near the north point of the horizon. Of course an explanation was wanted.

My assurance that there must be some mistake in the observation could not be accepted, because this erratic course of the heavenly body had been seen by all of them so plainly that no doubt could exist on the subject. The men who saw it were not of the ordinary untrained kind, but graduates of West Point, who, if any one, ought to be free from optical deceptions. I was confidently invited to look out that night and see for myself. We all watched with the greatest interest.

In due time the planet Mars was seen in the east making its way toward the south. "There it is!" was the exclamation.

"Yes, there it is," said I. "Now that planet is going to keep right on its course toward the south."

"No, it is not," said they; "you will see it turn around and go down towards the north."

Hour after hour passed, and as the planet went on its regular course, the other watchers began to get a little nervous. It showed no signs of deviating from its course. We went out from time to time to look at the sky.

"There it is," said one of the observers at length, pointing to Capella, which was now just rising a little to the east of north; "there is the star setting."

"No, it isn't," said I; "there is the star we have been looking at, now quite inconspicuous near the meridian, and that star which you think is setting is really rising and will soon be higher up."

A very little additional watching showed that no deviation of the general laws of Nature had occurred, but that the observers of previous nights had jumped at the conclusion that two objects, widely apart in the heavens, were the same.

Those words came from a book called "Reminiscences of an Astronomer," published in 1903 by Simon Newcomb, who was in charge of the American *Nautical Almanac* office from 1877 until 1897. The event actually occurred in 1860. The similarity to modern UFO's is overpowering. A star cavorting across the sky! Military officers as responsible witnesses!

In his delightful book, *Light and Colour in the Open Air,* the well-known Dutch astronomer, M. Minnaert, wrote.

"Moving Stars.

"In the year 1850 or thereabouts, much interest was aroused by a mysterious phenomenon; when one looked intently at a star, it sometimes seemed to swing to and fro and to change its position. The phenomenon was said to be observable only during twilight, and then only when the stars in question were less than 10° above the horizon. A brightly twinkling star was first seen to move with little jerks, parallel to the horizon, then to come to a standstill for five or six seconds and to move back again in the same way, etc. Many observers saw it so plainly that they took it to be an objective phenomenon, and tried to explain it as a consequence of the presence of hot air striae.

"But any real physical phenomenon is entirely out of the question here. A real motion of ½° per second, seen by the naked eye, would easily be magnified to 100° or more, by a moderately powerful telescope; that means that the stars would swing to and fro and shoot across the field of vision like meteors. And every astronomer knows that this is sheer nonsense. Even when atmospherical unrest is at its worst the displacement due to scintillation remain below the limit of perceptibility of the naked eye. Psychologically speaking, however, the phenomenon has not lost any of its importance. It may be due to the fact of there being no object for comparison, relative to which the star's position can be easily observed. We are not aware that our eye continually performs little involuntary movements, so that we naturally ascribe displacements of the image over our retina to corresponding displacements of the source of light.

"Somebody once asked me why a very distant aeroplane appears invariably to move with little jerks when followed intently with the eye. Here the same psychological cause obviously comes into play, as in the case of the 'moving' stars, and 'very distant' seems to point to the fact that this phenomenon, too, occurs most of all near the horizon.

"And how can we account for the fact that, suddenly and simultaneously, three people saw the moon dance up and down for about thirty minutes?"

This is the phenomenon of "Telekinesis," the apparent erratic motion of an object caused by the erratic motion of the human eye. I have seen a number of UFO reports in which the observer stated that the object could not have been a meteor or a satellite because it moved irregularly.

For you who wear eyeglasses there is still another way of seeing a UFO. Look directly at some bright light, with your head turned slightly to the left or right. You will probably see a faint roundish out-of-focus spot. This is light reflected from the front surface of your eyeball, back to the lens, and then back into the pupil of your eye. A bright source, to one side and slightly behind you, can also reach your eye through reflection from the internal surface of the spectacle lens.

To this moment I have not mentioned still another method of detecting saucers—one not subject to the vagaries of the human eye. I mean radar, of course. Radar is a machine. It can't make mistakes. Or at least that is the common argument advanced by UFO buffs.

Radar is cursed with all the potential afflictions that any complicated electrical gadget can suffer. But let me mention only one: mirage. Let me explain briefly what a radar does. It sends out a pulse of radio waves. We know the direction, Northeast for example. We know the elevation above the horizon. An echo returns. From the interval between transmission and reception of the pulse, we know how far away the object is that reflected the pulse back to us. We think we detect a plane—or a UFO in flight —because the radar directs the pulse upward.

We have no way of following the pulse in its path toward the target. A layer of warm, dry air or even a layer containing a few bubbles of warm air will bend the radar beam back to earth. The reflection may be from a distant building, a train, or a ship. No wonder that planes, sent to intercept radar UFO, find nothing. In one such case, a well-known writer on flying saucers wrote: "The discovery of *visible* saucers had been serious enough. —The discovery now of invisible flying saucers would be enough to frighten anyone." Small changes in the atmosphere can make the UFO seem to maneuver at fantastic speeds, executing right-angle turns or suddenly vanishing completely from the radar scope. I was very familiar with such effects from having worked with them during Naval Service in World War II. The greatest radar saucer flap of all times occurred in the hot, dry month of July 1952, when a whole fleet of UFO's were detected by radar at Washington National airport. Subsequent research by the Weather Bureau completely confirmed what the UFO buffs pointedly refer to as my "Hot Air Theory." After all why should one be surprised to find hot air over Washington?

I know of no reliable case of simultaneous visual and radar sightings. In view of the physical properties of the eye, the surprising fact is that so few cases have been reported.

Time will not permit me to elaborate on still other relevant phenomena. For example the Air Force appears to have neglected completely the psychological angle of which mass hallucination is just one phase. Back in 1919, in Spain, a not unrelated phenomenon occurred. Thousands of people—reliable people—swore that they had seen images of saints rolling their eyes, moving their hands, dripping drops of blood, even stepping out of their panels. One person would call out, others would imagine they had seen something! There are many similar events recorded through the ages.

There are hundreds of known hoaxes, such as the ingenious one perpetrated by students of the University of Colorado. Spurred by the allotment of an Air Force grant for studying UFO's to the University of Colorado, enterprising pranksters made hot-air balloons from candles and plastic bags, the kind used for packaging dry cleaning. The show was spectacular. And it gave the University investigators a good opportunity to see how poor the evidence can be, a fact well-known to the legal profession. This is still another point that the Air Force has sometimes failed to realize. Moreover their poor questionnaire only further confused an already confused picture. A recent similar sighting south of Denver, later identified as plastic-bag balloons and candles, produced fantastic reports from "reliable" witnesses.

Several times I have used the phrase "UFO's cavorting across the sky." I did so deliberately because it seems to be a favorite phrase of my good friend Dr. J. Allen Hynek of Northwestern University and consultant to the Air Force Project Blue Book. He has sometimes expressed doubts about the UFO because stars don't "cavort" across the sky. What I have tried to show is that many kinds of optical stimuli can produce weird effects.

With all these kinds of phenomena masquerading as UFO's, many of them, like those related to physiology of the human eye still practically not investigated, I think I can reasonably claim, applying the criterion of Sherlock Holmes, that we have not excluded all the impossibles. I have shown that the arguments advanced in favor of the interplanetary nature of UFO's are fallacious. Their alleged high speeds and ability to maneuver have completely natural explanations.

I think the time has come for the Air Force to wrap up Project Blue Book. It has produced little of scientific value. Keeping it going only fosters the belief of persons that the Air Force must have found something to substantiate belief in UFO's. In making this recommendation I am not criticizing the present or recent administration of the project. But it is time that we put an end to chasing ghosts, hobgoblins, visions, and hallucinations.

More than twenty years of study by the Air Force and an additional year of analysis by the University of Colorado have disclosed no tangible evidence supporting the popular view that UFO's are manned interplanetary vehicles. An irresponsible press, which has overpublicized the sensational aspects of the phenomenon, has been largely responsible for keeping the subject alive. Both newspapers and leading magazines must bear the blame for mishandling the news. But such publications are not scientific journals. They present incomplete data and draw sensational conclusions without supporting evidence.

The question of UFO's has become one of faith and belief, rather than one of science. The believers do not offer additional clear-cut evidence. They repeat the old classical cases and base the reliability of the sighting on the supposed honesty of the observer. I have shown that many honest observers can make honest mistakes.

The press has recently played up a story to the effect that, even in the U.S.S.R., an official UFO investigation has been started, under government sponsorship. Nothing could be farther from the truth! But the newspapers failed to retract after an official statement from the National Academy of the U.S.S.R. appeared in Pravda, to the effect that the reported study was the work of an unofficial and irresponsible amateur-group. The Academy statement further disclaimed any support whatever for the view that UFO's are other than badly misinterpreted natural phenomena, and certainly not manned extraterrestrial vehicles.

I am aware that a small but highly vociferous minority of individuals are pressing for further studies of UFO's supported—of course—by huge congressional appropriations. The heads of a few amateur UFO organizations urge their members to write

Congress, asking for investigations of both UFO's and the Air Force. The members have responded enthusiastically, and Congress reacted by financing a special study, which led to the project at the University of Colorado. And now, when it seems likely that the report from this study will be negative, the same vociferous group is again turning to Congress with the same appeal but with no more chance of success. Time and money spent on such efforts will be completely wasted. Congress should strongly disapprove any and all such proposals, large or small. In this age, despite the doubts expressed by a very small group of scientists, reopening and reopening the subject of UFO's makes just about as much sense as reopening the subject of Witchcraft.

Within the vast field of atmospheric physics, there exist many imperfectly understood phenomena which deserve further study, such as ball lightning and atmospheric optics. But any investigations of such phenomena should be carried out for their own sake, not under the cloak of UFO's.

I express my appreciation to Congressman Roush for the invitation to present my views on UFO's. I append herewith my telegram to him dated July 24, 1968.

JULY 24, 1968.

# Appendix II

A CONTRASTING written statement, among the others, was filed by Stanton Friedman, the Fellow Scientist at the Westinghouse Astronuclear Laboratory in Pittsburgh, who took his master's degree at the University of Chicago, and has gone on to specialize in radiation shielding and nuclear instrumentation. He is one of the scientists who feel that the UFO evidence points unmistakably to the fact that the earth is being surveyed by intelligently controlled extraterrestrial vehicles. Like most intelligent observers, he further agrees that *most* of the sightings can be explained by natural phenomena, but that the residue of carefully-documented observations are the ones that count. He points out that studies done half a dozen years ago at the Jet Propulsion Laboratory show that trips to the stars in reasonable times are actually feasible with the knowledge we have today.

In his statement, Friedman poses many penetrating questions. Among them, he answers such frequently-heard inquiries as: Are there any good unknowns? Why hasn't the worldwide Smithsonian Network of Satellite Tracking cameras picked up UFOs? Are the reported maneuvers of UFOs in violation of existing laws of physics? Haven't astronomers proved that trips to the stars are impossible?

There are many others, which with Friedman's answers, make up a compact review of the status of the UFO subject as seen by a scientist who maintains an open mind.

With this attitude he stands in sharp contrast to the Condon-Menzel school, the conclusions of which bog down in such obvious contradictions it is difficult to see how such credence is granted to them.

An important point Friedman does bring up, however, is that he does agree with Klass on one item, and that is that plasma glow may well *be associated with* the vehicles. Plasma alone does not by any means account for the scores of reliable UFO observations. Klass himself never considers this extension of his own theory. Friedman's overall feeling about Condon, Menzel and Klass is that it seems obvious that they are trying to make the data fit hypotheses rather than "trying to do the more difficult job of creating hypotheses that fit the data."

Mr. Friedman's statement was presented with a great number of appendices and references; these would not benefit the general reader, and have been omitted.

## PREPARED STATEMENT BY STANTON T. FRIEDMAN
### UFOs AND SCIENCE

I am grateful to the House Committee on Science and Astronautics for inviting me to present my views on Unidentified Flying Objects. These viewpoints shall be presented in the form of answers to specific questions with the references, tables and figures presented at the end of the article. A partial list of the technical organizations to which I have presented a lecture entitled "Flying Saucers are Real" is given in Appendix 1. Appendix 3 is a reprint of an article I wrote. Appendix 2 is a list of patents of saucer-like vehicles. The viewpoints are mine and mine alone and are not to be construed as those of any of the organizations to which I belong or of my employer, Westinghouse Astronuclear Laboratory. The opinions are based upon ten years of study of UFOs and discussions all over the U.S. and in Canada on a private level for eight years and a public level since late 1966 both in question and answer sessions following my illustrated talks and with newspaper, radio, and television reporters with whom I have publicly discussed the subject.

1. To what conclusions have you come with regard to UFOs?

I have concluded that the earth is being visited by intelligently controlled vehicles whose origin is extraterrestrial. This doesn't mean I know where they come from, why they are here, or how they operate.

2. What basis do you have for these conclusions?

Eyewitness and photographic and radar reports from all over the earth by competent witnesses of definite objects whose characteristics such as maneuverability, high speed, and hovering, along with definite shape, texture, and surface features rule out terrestrial explanations.

3. Haven't most sightings been identified as conventional phenomena?

Yes, of course. However, it is only the *unidentified* objects in which I am interested and on which I base my conclusions. The job of science is to sort data and focus on that which is relevant to the search at hand. Fewer than 1% of Americans have hemophilia or are 7 feet tall or can run a mile in under 4 minutes—we certainly don't dispute the reality of hemophilia, Wilt Chamberlain, or 4 minute miles.

4. Are there any good unknowns?

Yes, there are very many good unknowns which have been reported and investigated and undoubtedly very many more which have not been reported because of the "laughter curtain." In the most comprehensive detailed scientific investigation ever conducted on this subject, and reported in Reference 3, it was found that 434 out of 2199 sightings evaluated had to be classified as Unknowns. This is 19.7% or a far higher percentage than most people have associated with UFOs. The complete breakdown is shown in Table 1. Table 2 shows the breakdown of

### TABLE 1.—CATEGORIZATION OF UFO SIGHTING REPORTS[1]

| Category | Number | Percent |
|---|---|---|
| Astronomical | 479 | 21.8 |
| Aircraft | 474 | 21.6 |
| Balloon | 339 | 15.4 |
| Other | 233 | 10.6 |
| Unknown | 434 | 19.7 |
| Insufficient information | 240 | 10.9 |
| Total | 2,199 | 100 |

[1] Data from reference 3.

### TABLE 2.—QUALITY DISTRIBUTION OF UNKNOWNS

| Quality | Number | Percent of total | Unknowns | Percent of group |
|---|---|---|---|---|
| Excellent ..... | 213 | 9.7 | 71 | 33.3 |
| Good ......... | 757 | 34.5 | 188 | 24.8 |
| Doubtful ..... | 794 | 36.0 | 103 | 13.0 |
| Poor ......... | 435 | 19.8 | 72 | 16.6 |
| Total ..... | 2,199 | 100.0 | 434 | 19.7 |

sightings by quality. Fully one third of the 9.7% of the sightings labelled as Excellent were identified as Unknowns: one fourth of the Good sightings were labelled Unknown. All it would take to prove the reality of extraterrestrial vehicles is one good sighting not hundreds.

5. Aren't most of those "unknowns" really sightings for which insufficient data is available to identify an otherwise conventional object?

Absolutely not. If there was not enough information available about a sighting it was labelled "Insufficient Information" not "Unknown"—again contrary to what many people believe about UFOs.

6. Were there any differences between the Unknowns and the knowns?

A "chi square" statistical analysis was performed comparing the Unknowns in this study to all the "knowns." It was shown that the probability that the unknowns came from the same population of sighting reports as the knowns was less than 1%. This was based on apparent color, velocity, etc. Maneuverability, one of the most distinguished characteristics of UFOs, was not included in this statistical analysis.

7. Weren't most sightings of very short duration, say less than a minute?

The average duration of the sightings labelled as "Unknown" was greater than that for the knowns. More than 70% of the unknowns were under observation for more than 1 minute and more than 45% for more than 5 minutes.

8. Isn't it true that UFOs have never been sighted on radar? No, it is not. Ref. 3 specifically mentions radar unknowns. In Ref. 4, Edward Ruppelt, former head of the official UFO investigative effort, makes specific mention of not only "Unknowns" observed on radar but of combined visual and radar "Unknowns." Hynek also mentions radar and visual sightings.

9. Where can I get more information about "Unknowns"? Ref. 6 presents an unbiased description of about 160 "Unknowns." Ref. 7 includes data on over 700 Unknowns. References 8 and 9 contain many others.

10. Why haven't the worldwide Smithsonian Network of Satellite Tracking cameras picked up "Unknowns"? The former head of the film evaluation group concerned with the Smithsonian sky watch said that the purpose of the search was to get data on satellite orbits. If a light source on the film could be shown not to be a satellite then no further measurements were made. 10% to 15% of the plates showed anomalous light sources which were *not* a satellite but were not otherwise identified.

11. How about the other space surveillance radar installations? Baker in Ref. 11 deals with this question in detail. In summary, the systems are set up to reject signals which refer to anything other than the objects of interest—typically ballistic missiles coming from certain directions.

12. Aren't the reported maneuvers of UFOs in violation of existing laws of physics? Not at all. This argument ("It's Impossible") is used when what should really be said is we don't know how to duplicate these maneuvers. Piston aircraft can't fly faster than the speed of sound and a conventional dynamite bomb couldn't have wrecked Hiroshima and a vacuum tube circuit can't fit on the head of a pin but surely we don't say that supersonic flight, atom bombs and microcircuits violate the laws of nature or physics. Present aircraft can't duplicate UFO maneuvers; no laws of physics have been violated by UFOs.

13. Haven't astronomers proved that trips to other stars are impossible?

Again, the answer is no. The studies that conclude that trips to other stars are impossible are based upon false or unnecessary assumptions such as, assuming, that the flight be at orbital velocity. The one comprehensive study of interstellar travel conducted by a JPL group actually concerned with space hardware concluded that with present technology trips to nearby stars are feasible with round trip times being shorter than a man's lifetime and *without* violating the laws of physics. They assumed that stage vehicles would be used having either fission or fusion propulsion systems.

14. Are fission and fusion propulsion systems actually being developed?

Both fission and fusion propulsion systems for space travel are under development. I have worked on both. The NEVRA program has successfully tested a number of nuclear rocket reactors suitable for use in flight throughout the solar system. Flight rated systems offering substantial advantages over chemical propulsion systems could be ready in less than a decade if the current program at Aerojet General, Westinghouse Astronuclear Laboratory, and Los Alamos Scientific Laboratory is supported. References 15 and 16 are good reviews of the nuclear rocket program. The fusion work is not nearly as far along but has been productive at Aerojet General Nucleonics, San Ramon, California. An older review of some of the aspects of this program is given in Ref. 17.

15. Are these the only possibilities?

Not at all. This is one of the major flaws in the "non-believers" arguments; they presume that our technology is the ultimate—a presumption made by each generation of scientists in the last 75 years and proved wrong by the next generation of engineers and applied scientists. If there is one thing to be learned from the history of science it is that there will be new and unpredictable discoveries comparable with, say, relativity, nuclear energy, the laser, solid state physics, high field superconductivity, etc. It is generally accepted that there are civilizations elsewhere which are much more advanced than are we. Look what technological progress we have made in the last 100 years. Who can guess what we will accomplish in the next thousand years—or what others have accomplished in the thousand or million or billion year start they may have on us. We still don't know about gravity, for example, no less anti-gravity.

16. Could UFOs be coming here from our own solar system?

They certainly could. We have no data from any other body in the solar system which definitely rules out the existence of advanced civilizations. We frequently forget that the resolution of present photographs of the other planetary bodies is extremely poor. As a matter of fact, there does seem to be a direct correlation between the number of sighting reports per unit time and the closeness of Mars to the earth. Both have periodicities of about 26 months. We make certain space shots at "favorable times." The reverse may also be true but without the restrictions on payload and trajectory placed upon us by our crude, inefficient, space propulsion systems which no thoughtful engineer considers the ultimate.

17. Didn't the Mariner IV pictures prove there isn't any life on Mars?

The Mariner pictures didn't provide proof of life on Mars but they certainly didn't rule it out and were not intended to. Studies of 10,000 pictures of earth taken from orbit with cameras having resolving power equivalent to those on Mariner IV provided only one picture which could be taken to indicate that there is life on the planet called earth.

18. Isn't it true that life as we know it cannot exist on any other body in the solar system?

This statement, though repeated many times, is quite obviously untrue. Consider for a moment the fact that we intend to send men to the moon and by the end of the century to Mars. We expect these men to stay for a while and to return despite the fact that Mars and them on both supposedly aren't fit for life as we know it. One characteristic of an advanced technological civilization is the ability to provide suitable conditions for life almost anywhere; including under the ocean, in the void of space and on the surface of the airless, waterless moon and Mars. More and more we are also finding that life exists under almost all circumstances.

19. If we are being visited why haven't they landed?

The fact of the matter is that there are many reports of landings. The comprehensive study by scientist J. Vallee reviews 200 landings which occurred in 1954 alone; many of them with multiple witnesses giving reports of humanoids in addition to strange craft either on or just above the ground. Most scientists have unfortunately not examined this data since it was published in a UFO Journal and laughter comes easier than facing up to the evidence.

20. Has the attitude of the scientific journals and professional community been changing?

There has been a quiet yet enormous change in the attitude of the technological community. I say technological to include the applied scientists and engineers who are far more responsible for the progress of the last 30 years than the academic scientists who are prone to tell us all that is impossible. Examples of the change include the publication of articles by Science Astronautics and Aeronautics, the Journal of the Astronautical Sciences, the American Engineer, Industrial Research, Scientific Research, Aviation Week and Space Technology. In addition, numerous pro-UFO talks have been presented to local and national meetings of professional groups and the American Association for the Advancement of Science is planning a UFO seminar for a national meeting. The AIAA has even set up a UFO Committee.

21. Have there really been any electromagnetic effects associated with UFO sightings?

Indeed such reports are numerous, see for example Ref. 38, which includes stopping of car engines and headlights, and interference with radio and TV reception, magnetic speedometers, and watches.

22. Could these conceivably be related to a propulsion scheme?

There is an enormous amount of work available concerned with magnetoaerodynamics. I received a NASA bibliography with more than 3000 references. Ref. 39 contains abstracts of more than 800 publications dealing with interactions between vehicles and plasmas. Much of this work is classified because ICBM nose cones are surrounded by plasmas. In any event, there

is a body of technology which I have studied and which leads me
to believe that an entirely new approach to high speed air and
space propulsion could be developed using the interaction between magnetic fields with electrically conducting fluids adjacent
to the vehicles to produce thrust or lift and reduce or eliminate
such other hypersonic flight problems as drag, sonic boom, heat-
ing, etc. These notions are based on existing technology such as
that included in Ref. 40 through 49 though one would expect
that a considerable development effort would be required.

23. Have any electromagnetic propulsion systems been operated?

So far as I know no airborne system has been operated which
depended on electromagnetic forces for propulsion. At Northwestern, turning on a magnet inside a simulated re-entry vehicle
with a plasma around it resulted in a change in the color of the
plasma and its location relative to the vehicle. However, an
electromagnetic submarine has actually been built and successfully tested. It is described in some detail in References 50–52.

24. Can an EM submarine really be related to a UFO?

Dr. Way's electromagnetic submarine which, incidentally, is
silent and would be quite difficult to detect at a distance is directly analogous to the type of airborne craft I envision except
that the shape of the aircraft would most likely be lenticular and
the electrically conducting seawater would be replaced with an
electrically conducting plasma of ionized air.

25. Would lenticular vehicles fly?

I certainly think so. We seem to believe that airplanes have the
only possible shape probably because the Wright brothers plane
had the same outline which in turn was like that of birds. As
pointed out by Chatham in Ref. 53, flight is still only a byproduct
of high forward velocity leading to the need for long runways
and high speed landings and takeoff. Present airplanes are quite
obviously inefficient in terms of fuel consumption, payload fraction, and volume of air and airport space per passenger. After
all the SST will only carry a few hundred passengers though it
will occupy the space of a football field capable of holding at
least ten times as many people. Fuel weight is greater than payload weight and neither is a very high fraction of system weight.

It is interesting to note that most scientific progress has come from doing things differently rather than using the same technique—microcircuits aren't just smaller vacuum tubes; lasers aren't just better light bulbs. Many people are not aware that the U.S. Patent Office has granted more than ten patents for what one might honestly call flying saucer shaped craft all of which claim great maneuverability and the ability to rise vertically. Some can supposedly hover. None of these use magneto-aerodynamic techniques.

26. Have any members of your audience seen any UFOs?

I have taken to asking whether any members of my audiences have seen what they would call a UFO. Typically 3–10% are willing to raise their hands and usually there are others who approach me privately. These data, though limited, tend to support the Gallup Poll of 1966 which revealed that 5 million adult Americans claimed to have observed a UFO. Interestingly enough the official files contain fewer than 12,000 reports.

27. Were these sightings by your audience reported to investigative bodies?

In general, no. At Los Alamos Scientific Laboratory 25 of the 600 listeners indicated that they had seen something odd but only one had reported what he had seen.

28. Is there some way to get more data about UFOs besides reading reports?

There are several approaches that should be taken.

(a) Lift the "laughter curtain" so that more observers are willing to report what they see and more scientists will become involved.

(b) Using existing technology establish instrumented investigative teams and automated observation instrumentation such as that recommended by Dr. Baker before the Committee on Science and Astronautics.

(c) A world wide communication and study effort should be begun.

(d) A very large survey should be conducted to determine the characteristics of the objects that have been observed. The most comprehensive picture we have of ball lightning resulted from carefully conducted surveys by McNally and Rayle. UFOs in my opinion are definitely not ball lightning or other natural plasmas but are analogous to ball lightning and earthquakes in that their appearance cannot be predicted and they cannot be reproduced in the lab or in the field but they have been observed.

29. Are there any other references of interest to scientists?
Yes, References 56–62.

30. Haven't you biased your comments by not discussing at any length the work of Marcowitz, Menzel, and Klass?

The paper by Marcowitz and the books by Menzel, and Klass will undoubtedly be read by scientists of the 21st century as "classics" illustrating a non-scientific approach to UFOs by people who, for whatever reason, would not examine the data relevant to UFOs, or advanced technology. Marcowitz was totally wrong about fission and fusion propulsion systems, didn't even consider electromagnetic propulsion, and was obviously unaware of current technology and the data such as I mentioned earlier about UFOs. McDonald has discussed Menzel's approach in detail, but let me also point out that in Ref. 64, fewer than 30 sightings ever listed as "unknowns" were discussed and no mention was made of the 434 "Unknowns" of Ref. 3 or even the 71 Excellent Unknowns of this study. I agree with Klass on only one item, many people have observed glowing plasmas: but I believe they were adjacent to vehicles rather than ball lightning or corona discharge. He didn't even consider this possibility despite all his talk about plasmas and despite the enormous amount of plasma-vehicle data which is available. In summary, I feel that these three gentlemen have made strong attempts to make the data fit their hypotheses rather than trying to do the much more difficult job of creating hypotheses which fit the data.